99

The Coffee Tea or Me Girls' 'Round-the-World Diary

The Coffee Tea or Me Girls' 'Round-the-World Diary

Trudy Baker and Rachel Jones

GROSSET & DUNLAP
A NATIONAL GENERAL COMPANY
Publishers · New York

To DONALD BAIN

Contents

"Bless the child, so innocent and yet so assured in our adversity, her smile a citadel of strength in which I could be brave. My knuckles, bloodless as they gripped the armrest, only reflected the fear on my face, indeed within my heart itself. Sweet girl. Mother of calm. Her walk steady, eyes clear and positive, feet planted firmly against the airplane's buffeting, a soothing coo at the baby in frightened mother's arms, a gentle pat of courage on the old man's shoulder, an ever-so-slight wink at the soldier fresh from the jungles of Vietnam. Angel of mercy. Give me the fiber and fortitude in this hour of airborne need. The plane straining against the unseen forces of heaven as they lift us to near heights of fear and hysteria. All but you, precious lady. A rock of beauty and confidence. And then, suddenly, the smooth air returns and we glide home, giant silver bird touching neatly on the concrete ribbon. Sweet girl. Stewardess, they call you. Air hostess. Saint, I call you. Sweet little bird of confirmation. Lovely lass. Protector. Savior. Service beyond the bonds of duty as we walk together from the plane. Quiet drinks. Your layover. Pleasant motel. Bliss. Really a great piece."

Anonymous airline passenger to
anonymous airport bartender
1970

CHAPTER I

"Here We Go Again"

To stew or not to stew? Every airline stewardess is faced with that monumental decision many times during her flying career, usually coming in more frequent bursts towards the end of each year of service. Those of you who read our first book will recall Trudy and I deciding to give flying one more year.

We came to that joint decision for one very basic and easily understood reason: We hadn't found Mr. H. Gorgeous Right. No virile, outstanding male climbed on board our jets and swept us off our feet. And let's face it, folks, that's what stewardessing is all about.

Naturally, you can't go on forever in search of your airborne Romeo. It begins to tell on you after awhile. Pretty soon everything about you says you haven't found a proper mate, and that plays absolute havoc with your ego. But Trudy and I took hard-nosed looks at ourselves and decided it wasn't showing too much.

Trudy and I have been together for a long time. She's a tiny button-eyed brunette Taurus who always wonders if blondes *do* have more fun. I'm a rangy blonde Pisces who occasionally wishes she were a tiny brunette. And so it goes with most people.

We graduated together from stewardess college too long ago, signed on with a domestic airline as combination hatchicks, babysitters, airborne hashslingers and occasional amateur B-girls (No, you dirty old man, the B stands for Boeing). We fly together, live together, get in and out of trouble together and wrote our first book together. So it's only natural we put our heads together when the annual decision had to be made whether to continue the manhunt at 30,000 feet or give it up for new hunting grounds. You must keep in mind that the actual job of stewardessing falls somewhere in between the wildly glamorous job it seemed to be when we were dreamy teenagers, and the sour routine of the ten-year veteran stew. It's madly exasperating, divinely enervating, extremely weird at times, painfully funny, wildly unpredictable and . . . it's also better than the alternatives we came up with:

1. Turn in one uniform for another . . . join the Army. Lots of men there.

2. Become a plumber's apprentice and join the union.

3. Become a prostitute and go to Alaska.

4. Build up our bodies and join the Chicago police force as meter maids.

5. Learn enough about economics to misjudge the economy and become customer ladies in a brokerage house.

With the drawbacks to each alternative obvious, we decided to stick it out in the air. But, due to circumstances beyond our immediate control, forces were at work against us. We scented the pending problem upon returning from a Los Angeles-New York flight. Two identical perforated yellow missives awaited us in the boxes bearing our names in the operations center at Kennedy Airport. The messages were also identical: REPORT TO THE DIRECTOR OF STEWARDESS PERSONNEL TOMORROW AT 0900 HOURS.

What had we done? We did a quick mental rundown on the past few weeks. Neither of us had spilled any drinks on any passengers. No one had threatened to write nasty letters to management. Our individual weights were within regulation limits. Our hair had not progressed beyond the styles deemed appropriate by the airline, and we hadn't been caught drinking within twenty four hours of a flight. Maybe it was a mistake.

Maybe they got us mixed up with two foul-ups in the stew corps. No, not with both of us receiving the same notices. It was probably just some silly little infraction of some silly little rule that didn't mean anything. We dismissed all worrisome thoughts from our minds and slept like babes that night.

We walked into the stewardess personnel office at 9 A.M. the following morning right on time, and were met by a whole cast of official characters. There was no way to dismiss the courtroom atmosphere of the scene. We looked around and realized the only brass missing was the airline's president, although we wouldn't have been surprised to see him walk through the door at any moment.

Mr. Rakeman, director of all personnel for the airline, was in charge of the proceedings. This was obvious because he was sitting in the middle of everyone and kept clearing his throat in preparation for a speech.

Next to Rakeman was Maude Vestal, little mother of our stewardess corps, who tried to appear disinterested as she fidgeted with her lacquered hair.

But the real indication of trouble was the presence of Casey O'Shea, paid New York representative of our union. The personnel office never bothers her with trivial or routine matters. When Casey shows up, you can bet a hanging is in the wind.

We sat down opposite Mr. Rakeman and smiled to break the heavy ice. He lowered his eyes and cleared his throat some more.

"Well, what's up?" I chirped.

"I don't find this a pleasant occasion," Rakeman muttered. "Not pleasant at all." It seemed for the moment he was reprimanding us for smiling. I adopted a long face. So did Trudy. Maude Vestal's face dropped halfway to her cross-your-heart bra. Casey O'Shea was the only one keeping her chin up.

I didn't know what we were all supposed to be in

mourning about. But when Rakeman turned to me and called me "Miss Jones," I had an inkling. And when he called Trudy "Miss Baker," we both knew the jig was up. Each of those five-letter names were our *noms de plume.* We'd used them on our book, and only our publishers were supposed to be able to connect the names with our faces and chassis. Well, our mothers, too, but they didn't count in this hassle. Rakeman pronounced our pen names as though they were four-letter words unfit for mixed or unmixed company. Trudy tried not to look at me. I stared straight ahead. It was only seconds, but the silence dragged into eternity as Rakeman reached down to his lap and dragged up a dog-eared paperback copy of *Coffee Tea or Me?* Our book. Our little bestseller. He looked at it and held it away as if it were a particularly foul piece of old cheese.

"Wacky," he sneered with a nod to Maude Vestal. "Naughty," he added with a bow for Casey O'Shea. "Authentic," he snarled to us. He continued to read the copy off the dust jacket of the book as if it were a confession of murder and mayhem. And the way he dragged it out, milking each syllable! " 'The uninhibited memoirs of two airline stewardesses,' indeed Miss Baker," he shouted, looking at me. "And Miss Jones," he yelled at Trudy. He'd mixed up our pen names, but that wasn't the kind of legal loophole the two of us could wiggle through.

" 'Here's the real low-down,' " he began as he turned the book over and started reading from the back. I couldn't stand the recital any longer and cut in.

"We've read the book, Mr. Rakeman."

"So did three million other people," Trudy added.

It served its purpose. Rakeman stopped. He shook. His face turned purple. Finally he sputtered, "This piece of trash, this revolting libel, this . . . this . . . this . . ." and sank into blissful speechlessness.

"We thought it was kind of funny," I said, quickly

adding, "and it didn't really tell the truth about stewardesses." I looked to Maude Vestal for some sign of
belief. Her lips remained sealed, caked together with
paint. I turned to Casey. She smiled but said nothing.

Rakeman dropped the book on his desk and rose
grandly to his feet.

"Three million is an awful lot of people, Mr. Rakeman," Trudy said. "And lots of people enjoyed it. I
mean, no one *really* believed it and . . ."

"Enough!" Rakeman commanded, shaking even
Maude Vestal with the power of his voice.

I was glad he stopped Trudy. A lawyer beau of
mine once told me never to plead guilty to anything,
and I felt Trudy was coming dangerously close to cop-
ping a plea. But then a thought struck me. Maybe this
was all just a prelude to the news that we were going
to get a medal for stirring up interest in air travel.
Maybe they were going to make us stewardess-of-the-
year or something like that and put our pictures on
the cover of the house organ. Or on the in-flight menu,
at least.

"If anyone enjoyed this kind of trash, it certainly
wouldn't be anyone in the industry," Rakeman said.
"I should think you'd be ashamed at having smeared
the good names and reputations of so many of your
colleagues and fellow-workers." He was winding up,
heading for the summing up of his case. There was no
sense in trying to slide out from under now. It was
time to fight back and defend what we'd done.

"Mr. Rakeman," I said, trying desperately to remember how F. Lee Bailey spoke, "Our attorneys went
into this point at some length. They examined the Federal Air Regulations and the airline manual of regulations and found nothing to keep us from writing a
bestseller."

"I can assure you there soon will be such a regulation."

"I think that's silly, sir," Trudy said. "Jackie Kennedy tried to stop her cook from writing a book about her and look what happened."

"Yes," I added. "What if we quit and write *another* book? What can you do about that?"

Rakeman didn't answer. He stood there as though he were waiting for me to produce a letter of resignation from my blouse. If I had a hot one, I would have thrown it down in front of him.

"Miss Jones and Miss Baker," he said. "We are not discussing your rights under the First Amendment. What we are discussing is your responsibility as members of a profession serving the American public. A book that . . . a book that gives people a look at the wonders of this infant industry, a book that truly reflects the joy of working as a stewardess, a book that . . ." He was off into the wild blue yonder describing the kind of book he thought we ought to have written. I turned off my hearing aid. There was one of those books tucked into the back of every seat in every airplane, printed in six glorious colors, and I've never seen anyone read it yet. I told Mr. Rakeman that.

"We're sorry you didn't like it, Mr. Rakeman," Trudy said softly. He didn't respond. He just took his seat again and shook his head back and forth.

Enter Casey O'Shea into the dialogue. She stood up when Rakeman sat down. She came up behind us and put a hand on each of our shoulders. I never thought being squeezed by a girl could feel so good. Everyone had been so emotional. Casey was calm as a judge.

"The facts are, girls," she began, "the airline wants to fire you. That's why I'm here. It's my job to make sure no one pulls that kind of a Fascist trick and to see that you get a fair shake."

"Yes indeed," Rakeman broke in, hot under the collar and shouting like a tobacco auctioneer. "The union is always ready to protect girls who smoke in the galley and won't wear the cute little hats we pay so much to have designed for you and who steal the little bottles from the planes and . . ."

". . . and call in sick when all they're doing is lying in bed in the morning with some disgusting paramour," Maude Vestal added, her lower lip trembling.

"Who's libeling the industry now?" Casey yelled. "One more crack like that and we'll hit the bricks."

"Strike, strike, strike," Vestal whimpered. "That's all you know how to do."

"I tell you," Casey pressed. "You mistreat these girls and you'll have the biggest damned strike on your hands since we went out over the right to share apartments with men."

Things had gone just about as far as they could go. It was all in Casey's hands, as far as we were concerned. She was calling the signals and doing a pretty good job of it. When she walked to the door and put her hand on the knob, we knew what to do. We walked, too. There was no point in rubbing any more salt into the corporate wounds, real or imagined. When Casey didn't even say goodbye, we kept quiet, too.

"You were beautiful, Casey," I said when we got outside.

"Yes, Casey, just beautiful," said Trudy. "I feel like breaking into a chorus of the union hymn."

"Not yet, kids. Not yet."

Casey filled us in on the whole tale. The airline had hired some public relations men and paid them thousands of dollars to read our book and to advise the corporate brains on how to "handle" it . . . and us. They collected all the clues, decoded all the messages, psyched out all the traffic reports, took voice patterns on Trudy and me when we appeared on radio interviews and finally narrowed it down and discovered our true identities. The next step was to decide what to do with us. The public relations men advised the airline to be cool. If the airline fired us openly and directly, it might be a big scandal, the kind the newspaper and television people love. With a little help from our friends, if they fired us, we could have sold four million copies instead of three. So, the order was given to do nothing and ride it out.

"The big wigs paid a lot of money for smart advice," Casey suggested. "But that doesn't stop the little wigs like Rakeman and that bitch Vestal from getting into the act. They can't fire you but they sure want to shake you up and make you miserable. They'll be after you every second. They'll report every goof you make. If your hat isn't on at the right angle, eighteen people will break their necks reporting it. So don't start singing any songs. We're not out of the fogbank yet."

I told Casey we'd just decided to give flying one more year.

"Yeah," Trudy remembered. "Yesterday it was a hairline decision almost. But we're not quitting under fire. No, sir. They can't scare me. I'm sticking with the union right down the line."

"Me, too," I added.

Casey made a strange little expression which could have indicated pleasure at our solidarity or displeasure at having us in the union at all. We didn't try to analyze it. It was just good to be out of the courtroom, as tenuous as the bail might prove to be.

We discussed the situation that night with George Kelman, our favorite New York stew bum. George had become our father and protector ever since we were baby stews fresh out of stewardess school. In fact, he performed that function for half the stewardess corps in New York. But we were his favorites. No doubt about that at all. Trudy called him the minute we got back to the apartment and he arrived that evening toting a giant pepperoni pizza and beer. After he ate most of the pizza and we drank most of the beer, he became serious and thoughtful. He listened as we recalled the choreography of the confrontation at Kennedy. We told him everything we could remember. And then it was time for the old oracle to speak.

"They can't fire you kids," he said, stabbing at the air to make his point. "They know better. But here's what will happen. They'll be on your back every second. They'll write you up for every goof. Get one letter from one irate passenger and they'll string you up. Check in late once and they'll boil you in engine oil. And take one drink within the 24-hour limit and they'll drag you behind a 747 on takeoff."

It was grim having George confirm what Casey told us. We told him what she said.

"Yeah, and she's right. My suggestion is that you two start looking around for something else to do."

"Like what, George?"

"How do I know? Join the Army. Get a plumber's license and join the union."

"We've already decided not to do those things."

"Oh. Well, join another airline."

"Do you think we could?"

"It won't be easy, girls. I imagine the word is out around the industry that you two write big, bad books about the business. But I'll check a little and see what's up. Call you in a few days."

We worked two trips before talking to George again. One was a short hop to Cleveland and the other was to San Francisco. On both trips our friendly stewardess supervisor turned up on the passenger list wearing a black wig and sunglasses. She kept her little notebook in her lap the whole time. She hung out into the aisle checking the shine and heels of our shoes. She had her stopwatch going to check how long it took us to wheel the booze cart up and down the aisle. And we were called in after both flights and harangued for everything that happened, including being forced to listen to a taped recording of my arrival announcement at Cleveland in which I mispronounced the name of a new Polish flight engineer. We left the office fuming.

Trudy called George to let off some steam. He said he was about to call us anyway and came over with another pizza. It was cold and rubbery but he was bubbling with hot news. He had this pal at another airline who knew all about us and the book. But this pal liked to live dangerously. He was also constantly on the make for stewardesses, according to George, and was dying to meet the two girls who set the industry on its ear. He also happened to have some personal dirt on the guy at the airline in charge of all stewardess recruiting. This poor soul wouldn't dare refuse to hire any girl sent by George's friend.

"He'd like to see you girls," George told us. "You have to remember the bloom is off the glamour stuff in stewardessing. There's a shortage of good stews all over the industry. Let's face it, you two are experienced, pro stews. As for the book, it's been out for over a year now. You'll never write another one, and the airlines know it. The girls they have to worry about are the ones who are trying to imitate you by writing *their* memoirs."

"What do we have to do, George?" I asked. "We can't hack Vestal and Rakeman any more. So point the way to this other airline."

"OK, girls. I'll make an appointment for you to see my buddy, Charlie Wag. Now remember, he'll be expecting a couple of real swingers. You can go all out."

"What does that mean?" Trudy wanted to know.

"Well, Charlie has read the book and he figures you two for the all-time champion fun girls. You know, zingy, hip and loose. This is an international airline and these guys have really been around."

"*International* airline? You didn't tell us that."

"Just assumed you knew."

"Well, we didn't, George. But I'm glad it is," I said. "I think Trudy and I are much more the international type. We've just been wasted flying domestic all these years. Right, Trudy?"

She nodded emphatically.

"Besides," I went on, "the men who fly international would appreciate us more. Who knows, we might end up marrying some Italian prince or some British playboy or even an Arabian king."

"I'll take the playboy, Rach, OK?"

"We'll see," I answered.

"What should we wear when we meet Mr. Wag, George?"

"Go all out, girls. All out and way out."

We did. We shopped the mod spots and held a little preview fashion show for George the night before our appointment. We have to give George credit for burying his true feelings beneath his desire to help us land the job. George has always thought of *his* stews as good, relatively modest girls. He doesn't like stews who come off too hard or sexy. You can imagine how tough it was for him to say, "Gee, Rachel, I love the little leather dress with the cutouts in front. Charlie should really go for that."

Poor George. He had to bite his tongue before saying to Trudy, "A see-through blouse, Trudy. Really great." All the while George was probably envisioning Charlie Wag shifting his eyes from my cutouts to Trudy's see-through.

We didn't stop with clothes. We spent hours at a highly-touted hair dresser and had professional makeup jobs performed on us. When we arrived at Charlie Wag's office we were as ready for a screentest as we'd ever be. We were loaded with sensual confidence, as much as a hat check bunny at a disc jockey convention.

"Are you always so overdone?" Mr. Wag asked us as we sat across from him in his office.

"What do you mean by that?" I asked, trying to look coyly indignant.

"Well, you know how the airlines are. They want simple, fresh beauty, untouched loveliness. I hate to say it but you both look like Miami Beach in season."

Did we blow it? I was about to get up and call it a day when Mr. Wag smiled, got up and closed the door. "Frankly," he said, perching on the edge of his desk, "I really don't like all this simple beauty crap. I like girls who look like they've been around a little. You know what I mean?" He winked and lighted a long, thin cigar. We didn't respond, so he continued.

"George told me about your writing the book and all so I figure you *have* been around a little." He took a long, slow drag on the cigar.

"Not really," Trudy said. "You see . . ."

I jumped right in and cut off Trudy's defense of our virtue. "What she means is, Mr. Wag, is that we *have* been around a little. You know how it is, with the new morality and the hotels and all the male pressure we get. A girl just can't help but give in once in awhile."

"That's what I figured," Wag said, returning to his chair. "Look, don't get me wrong. I'm not saying you have to swing to get a job here. But hell, a guy has to have a little fun now and then. The way I figure it, we only have one shot at this old life and you never know when the bomb is going to fall and go booooom. Right? By the way, this isn't my own original philosophy. Have you read this?" He reached behind and came up with a leather-bound, initialed collection of Hugh Hefner's *Playboy Philosophy*.

"Yes, yes, we adore it." What else could I say?

"Hugh makes a lot of sense," Wag said grimly. "We've got to shake this damned puritanical hangup we have. Don't you agree?"

"Oh, yes. Of course, Trudy and I don't have that kind of hangup."

"I see. Good. All right, fill out these applications and I'll get them processed right away. In a few days, they'll be finalized and we can set a date for you to start with us. Then, we'll have a nice, little, intimate celebration at my place. OK?"

"Groovy," I sighed.

"Kicky," Trudy added.

"And call me Charlie. All the stews do, at least the ones I hang around with."

"OK, Charlie. And we sure do appreciate this. I hope we'll be able to show that appreciation to you soon." I couldn't believe this pap was coming from me.

"Later, ladies. At my place."

I winked at him and bent over to give him a better peek at my cleavage. Trudy pouted her lips a la Marilyn Monroe. Charlie Wag smiled and licked his lips.

Outside, we started giggling and kept giggling all the way back to the apartment. George was there.

"Well, you really did it, didn't you?" he said with disgust.

"We sure did, George, thanks to you. We've got a new job and we can tell Vestal and Rakeman to fluff off."

"Sure," George snarled. "And then betray my confidence in you by making a date to go to bed with that creep, Charlie Wag."

"What are you talking about?" Trudy demanded.

"I'll tell you, you traitors. Never once have I made a pass at you. Right?"

"Right, George. And we love you for that."

"So what do you do? I send you to a job to save your skins and you accept his invitation to go to his place. He called me and told me he made it plain to you that you'd have to sleep with him and the two of you told him it was fine. In fact, he said you indicated you couldn't wait."

We explained to George how we didn't argue when Wag invited us to celebrate with him.

"Sure," George mumbled. "Charlie thanked me for sending two real live ones and bragged he'd have both of you in his sack within the week. Together, maybe. He probably keeps notches on his bedpost."

George stayed mad for three weeks. It wasn't until Charlie Wag told him he hadn't scored with us yet that our favorite stew bum warmed up a little. By that time we'd given in our notices to the old airline and were packing to attend our new line's stewardess school for four weeks of training. It was a grim thought after having spent six weeks in school with the old line, but anything was better than continuing to operate under Rakeman and Vestal.

We breezed through the four weeks of school, kept our noses clean, started taking notes in case we ever decided to write another book, and came back to New York as working stews with the international carrier. George treated us to dinner when we got back and told us Charlie was furious at us for avoiding him. He pledged to George he'd have us in bed some day. His attempts at this over the next year kept our lives interesting, along with other factors that contributed to making this new flying job anything but dull.

The important thing was that we were now employed as international airline stewardesses. And although our previous experience with our old airline's reaction to our book writing was certainly unpleasant, we never missed a day of diary-keeping on this new job. And that's how this book you're reading came about.

So come along with us, traveler, through the maze of international travel, continental men, high flight and high living as we again take to the air. Our diary and hearts are yours.

CHAPTER II

"Another First Flight"

After stewardess school, we were assigned to reserve status for our first month of duty. All new stews get stuck with reserve status and it's a real pain in the proverbial neck. You're subject to call at any time, which means you have to be in a constant state of readiness. You can't make any personal plans that would take you away for even a day, and if you take a drink during the month, you'd better have a good supply of breath mints handy.

We were called to work a flight on the sixth day of our reserve stint. Two girls on a New York-Madrid run came down with the flu and we were assigned the flight. What surprised us was how nervous we became as flight time approached. You'd think that after working hundreds of flights with our former airline we'd be past the point of opening-flight jitters. But this was . . . international. We tried to reason away our nerves. We'd served many travelers from other lands on our domestic runs. But . . . The apprehension hung on.

Once we were airborne, however, it didn't take us long to get over those nerves. It was soon obvious that flying over the ocean was really no different than flying over Lake Erie. The 707 contained the same types of people, the good and the bad, the courteous and the rude, the old and the young. And men who fly to Madrid view airline stewardesses in the same light as Chicago-bound males. Each assumes his stew in her jazzy uniform is leading a madly exciting life. Her heart is in the clouds. Her chosen career is stimulating, free from the workaday monotony and boredom of earthbound creatures toiling behind typewriters and filing cabinets. There are no more Mondays with airline stewardesses, no more end-of-weekend blues and subways to catch with the rush-hour crowd. To the average passenger, the whole wide wonderful world is a stew's office and the sleek jets are her subways— with reserved seats yet. Days are filled with warm adventure and the romance of far-away exotic lands. Dashing men lead us on gay romps through all the nations of the earth. People yearn to travel in our pretty shoes, yearn to fly from Rangoon to Rome, Hong Kong to Helsinki, to Asia, Africa, and Europe and the glamorous cities of Latin America like Rio, or Havana, or Caracas, or Havana, or Montevideo, or Havana.

Too, our passengers envy our intimate contact with all the warm and lovable notables of the world. One day we might be serving blueberry cheese cake to Jackie Onassis and the next day serving scrambled eggs to Jack Carter. Or Chicken Kiev to Danny Kaye and Jack Paar. Or lobster tails to George Jessel and Jerry Lewis and all the other good guys.

In fact, when Trudy and I were fighting to retain our footing on a flight from New York to Louisville and being yelled at by heavy-equipment salesmen and punched by little kids and abused by heavy-handed mashers, *we* envied those sisters-of-the-skies who were serving the jet set from New York to Rome. It all proves one thing. The grass *is* always greener on the other side, and people can be soooooo wrong about how the other half lives. After just one hour on our Madrid flight, we knew right down to our aching insteps that flying with an international carrier meant no extra glamour, no additional kick, no secret pleasures. It's all the same, at least the on-board portion. Laying over in foreign ports of call might be different, but the 707 and its cabin full of human beings doesn't change.

Our first passenger to board the Madrid flight in New York was a little old lady. Actually, she didn't board the aircraft. She was carried by two young passenger agents, each with a firm grip on a wheel of her collapsible wheel chair. She waved her crutch around like a polo mallet. Her hair-do was protected from the elements by a net cap with a plastic bag over it. She was eighty if she was a day, and her mink stole wasn't much younger. The agents got her inside the cabin, unwrapped her and settled her into a window seat in the middle of the section.

"I think I'll be cold by the window," she said.

So we lifted her into a seat on the aisle.

"I think I'd like to be closer to the pilot," she said.

LITTLE OLD LADY SKYJACKS JET

I looked at her crutch and her pocketbook. Everyone else was trying it and maybe it was little-old-lady-week to go to Cuba. We decided it was better having her up front so we could keep an eye on her, even though all the incoming passengers would trip over her crutch. I also decided to get her name early and not have to hassle with it later, when the cabin noise level would be higher. I bent over sweetly, holding my clipboard and pencil.

"Your name, ma'am?"

"I'll have Jack Daniels on the rocks. And bring both of 'em at the same time, dearie."

"Yes, Mrs. Daniels."

It promised to be a bad trip.

Our first flight also had its share of kids. Kids are all right, provided their parents are all right. But high altitude seems to do something to parents. They become giddy and forget everything about discipline. One

little fellow in particular, a chunky four-year-old, insisted on laying prone in the middle of the aisle whenever we tried to pass. It delighted his parents. The
little fellow also made frequent trips to the aircraft
john armed with a plastic bag full of crayons. One
look at the john walls and there was little doubt we
had a young Portnoy with us. Not only did he write
on the walls with his greasy crayons, he enjoyed using
all the four-letter words known to modern man. His
particular brand of youthful graffiti was brought to our
attention by a nasty, middle-aged woman who told us
she didn't like airline stewardesses one bit.

"Why?" I asked stupidly.

"Because all the airlines care about is having vo-
luptuous sexpots as stewardesses. Now don't argue
with me, young lady. I know. Our daughter, Vera, was
turned down not only by your airline but by three
others. Her father and I were against the whole idea
in the first place but Vera is very mature and we allowed her to apply. Here, look at this picture and tell
me if Vera isn't a pretty and vivacious young lady . . .
if you can recognize a young lady." I looked at the
snapshot and saw a pudgy, pasty brat with watery eyes
and acute protruding teeth.

"She's lovely," I muttered.

"A good girl, too. But that's not what I wanted to
talk to you about. Have you been in the ladies' room
lately?"

"No." That's when I went in and saw the subject of
the woman's complaint. Sure enough, little Mr. Portnoy had told the world where to go in no uncertain
terms. All the words were there, strung together and
correctly spelled and blazing out in vivid red, orange
and purple.

"I see what you mean, ma'am," I said as I came out
of the john.

"Well, don't just stand there, do something. Wipe it

off before others have to be subjected to such filth."

"Yes, ma'am." I wiped away with paper towels but only managed to smear the colors around on the wall. The effect was psychedelic, but at least the words were obscured. Well, obscured until the little fellow returned to the john with his crayon bag. I caught him as he came out, his bag of crayons clutched tightly in his dirty little paws and a tight smile of defiance on his lips. I grabbed his arm and looked into the john. More words were scribbled, even on the toilet seat and window. I squeezed his arm. He started screaming. I marched him directly back to his mother and father.

"Your little boy has been writing with crayons all over the walls of the bathroom," I said quietly and calmly.

The mother and father laughed. "Yes, he is a devil," his mother said, chuckling. "Precocious, too." She gave his fat little nose a tweak and patted his head.

"You don't understand," I continued. "He's ruined the walls. But more important, he's been writing filthy words and upsetting other passengers."

The parents turned grim. I thought they were about to take some action with their offspring but it was soon obvious they were mad at me, not him.

"I resent what you've just said," the mother said.

"But it's true," I argued. "Come look."

We went up the aisle and opened the bathroom door. Trudy had just emerged after having wiped the walls again with towels. The mother looked inside at the multi-color smears and started lacing into me.

"There are no dirty words in there," she said with a hard edge to her voice.

"Not now there aren't, but there were. Miss Baker just wiped them off."

"It's a shame, a real shame that families can't fly together without having to be abused by snotty young

stewardesses who only want to serve bachelor men.
But we paid our money and demand courtesy for all
members of the family, including little, innocent children and wives."

That did it. I started to argue and the lady demanded my full name so she could write the airline
and complain about me. Trudy, standing behind her,
almost cried. I almost did, too.

As I mulled over being called on the carpet because
of the letter, the next typical passenger surfaced. He
was drunk. There is always one person drunk on
every flight. In some cases, people get drunk to help
overcome an inborn fear of flying. Others get to the
airport too early and drink to pass the time. And
then there are others who just drink all the time, on
the ground or in the air. This particular fellow fell
into the latter category. No doubt about that. His
sober breaths were few and far between.

All drunks aren't a problem on a flight. Those who
insist on smoking during takeoff can be nasty when
you tell them to put out the cigarette. Some drunks
make too blatant a pass at you and it's hard to reason
with a juiced-up Romeo. But this drunk on the Madrid
flight really didn't bother us. In fact, all he did was
ask for was a drink of water, but he caught Trudy in
the midst of meal preparation and she simply nodded
her head towards the drinking fountain. He stumbled
up the aisle, his pork pie hat perched on the top of his
head and his pants hanging around his hips like some
second banana in a burlesque show. Trudy promptly
forgot about him and I did too until I happened to
look to the rear of the cabin. There he was, hands
clamped around the lever that opens the rear exit
door. I flew up the aisle, grabbed him around the
shoulders and pulled him away.

"Is the water fountain in that room?" he asked,
with a silly smile.

"What room?" I snapped back.

"Behind that door," he belched.

"The only thing behind that door, mister, is 38-thousand feet of air."

"No room out there?" He seemed hurt and sad.

"No, sir. No room."

"Little airplane, isn't it?"

"Yup. Come on, I'll get you a drink of water if you promise to stay in your seat until we reach Madrid."

"I promise. I really promise."

He kept his word. The only further trouble we had with him was trying to shake him awake after landing in Madrid. "I promise," he moaned in his sleep. I had to smile. He was still promising to stay in his seat. Then he called me Molly a few times, and murmured, "I promise, Molly, I'll never touch another drop if you come back."

Yes, flying to Madrid was no different than flying to Rochester. We took care of kids, drunks and old ladies *and* kept a sharp lookout for handsome, young, unattached males. There were a couple on board but we suspected the masculinity of one of them. We went about our business of collecting empty drink glasses and flirting with the eligibles when a stern lady stopped me cold with an icy stare. She pointed to her tray. On it was a tiny red pamphlet, its cover stained from the condensation on an empty glass.

"Read this," she commanded.

I took it to the galley and Trudy and I read it together. Its title was *"Women Rise Up"* and it dealt with the growing tide of female liberation. This particular pamphlet was directed specifically at stewardesses.

"I hope she isn't going to skyjack the plane," I muttered to Trudy as we read. "If she does it in the name of females, I wonder where we'd go. Females don't have a country, do they?"

"Not the last time I heard, Rach."

The pamphlet was full of the standard agitation, telling us that in one state (it didn't mention which one specifically) in the U.S. a woman's clothing legally belonged to her husband; women receive 40 per cent less pay than men for the same jobs; there is only one woman in the U.S. Senate after fifty years of suffrage, while 74 per cent of the doctors in Russia are women. All this will change, the pamphlet promised, when women rise up.

Why can't we have women airline pilots? Let the men pour the drinks and change the diapers for a change.

That hit home.

We read on.

In modern commercial aviation, the role of women is typically degrading. Visit women's career day on a college campus. Big corporations are out there competing for male engineers and technicians. Nobody offers women anything but insulting jobs like nursing in the Army, tellers in banks and waitresses on airlines. Airlines make it plain women are unfit even to participate in the technicalities of flight. Airline Stewardesses are required to take training in the theory of flight, navigation, communications, emergency equipment and procedures, and then when they go out to work they are told to forget all they know and smile. There is no way for women to advance in aviation.

For women, another "glamorous" occupation turns out to be a deadend.

"How about that?" I sighed. "I never knew how mistreated I really was, Trudy."

"Me, neither."

The last page of the pamphlet cited recent psychiatric studies which showed that aggressive dominant women enjoy sex more than submissive women, contrary to popular myth. The other girls on the flight read the pamphlet and we spent the rest of the time debating that last page. We all argued our viewpoints until Trudy put the stopper on the bottle of debate.

"That may be true," she said. "But I wonder who they'll find to enjoy sex *with.*"

Good point, old pal.

We eventually got meals served to everyone and took our first real breather since takeoff. It again occurred to me to wonder why we expected it to be more glamorous flying international than domestic. Where were all the exciting jet-set celebrities we were supposed to trip over at every turn? If it hadn't been for the one little jewelry salesman who said *"Gracias, señorita"* to me when I handed him his tray, we might be heading for Roswell, New Mexico. And when he did speak to me, I thought it might be a trap. I thought he was some sort of company spy lurking there to smoke me out for having cheated on my foreign language exams at stew school.

We'll never forget that exam. We were on our way, thinking the four-week course would be a breeze, a boring re-hash on the six-week course we'd taken at the other airline. But when we discovered that our friend, Charlie Wag, had sworn on our applications that we both had "reasonable knowledge of one other language besides English" we panicked and bought a selection of do-it-yourself language books. We barely had the books cracked when the day came for the exams. We expected a written exam on which we could cheat easily. Instead, it turned out to be a conversational quiz with one of the faculty members. Fortunately, it wasn't alphabetical and we had a chance to ask some of the other girls what it was the instructor asked.

The girls told us that in each instance, the instructor asked them what they had for breakfast. In reply, the girls recited names of different foods in French or German or Spanish.

"But what do they ask after that?" we pressed our classmates.

Different questions, it turned out. Desperate, we called George long distance and asked his advice. Easy, he suggested, just make up a long story about how you couldn't eat breakfast because you were sick. Look up the words in a dictionary, copy them down and learn it word for word, just like a song. When they ask you what you had for breakfast, give them this whole spiel. Very fast. If you confuse them, they'll be very impressed because they probably don't know much more Spanish than you do. If they start asking more questions, grab your stomachs and moan some. Maybe keep saying the Spanish word for sick over and over. That should do it, he told us.

So that's what we did, and it worked. To this day, if anyone asks me what I had for breakfast, I reply with a long fast story in Spanish about stomach cramps and heartburn and Tums. Never fails to astound.

We landed in Madrid tired and dejected. No glamour. No celebrities. Nothing but sore legs and feet and a kink in the neck.

"Maybe the flight back will be better," Trudy suggested.

"Yeah, maybe."

It wasn't. But things did get better as we progressed to regular monthly schedules to far-off places. Our second month found us on the New York-Paris run. Paris in itself is interesting and enjoyable. It became even more so when we were introduced to Pierre Popinjois, the best-known stew bum in Paris. Through him, we discovered there exists a world-wide stew bum network, each member ready to welcome the favorite stews of a fellow-member.

CHAPTER III

"The Devaluation
of Pierre Popinjois"

stew bum; (stū bum) A male homo sapien addicted to the pursuit of airline stewardesses.
Usually young and in possession of relatively
large sums of money, the stew bum originated
in North America, although the species has been
found as far west as China and as far east as
Russia. Seldom dangerous, the stew bum attaches itself to its prey and clings tenaciously.
Prevalent in larger apartment buildings in which
airline stewardesses live (known as stew zoos).

It was impossible to control our laughter. There
we were, the eight of us, weathered in at Orly Field,
Paris, sitting at the coffee shop counter and holding
our stomachs and aching sides and wiping the tears
away. All the other patrons of the coffee shop looked
on in amusement as the two El Al girls bit their lips
and stomped their feet and the two SAS stews shrieked
with glee. That only accounts for six of us, however.
The remaining two people in our party, Pierre Popinjois and his friend, Henri, sat sullenly, their eyes fixed
on the countertop. Henri took an occasional suck from
a peeled orange and threw us little nervous smiles.
Pierre did and said nothing. I guess he was still in
shock at seeing us all together. Never in his wildest
dreams did he think we'd meet up with the girls from
El Al and SAS and compare notes on the previous
evening in Paris. It had been quite an evening for all
of us, but especially for Pierre and Henri who played
the major roles in each of our Parisian adventures.

Pierre Popinjois is a French stew bum. We were injected into his life by George Kelman, our favorite New York stew bum. After flying the New York-Paris run for two weeks, George decided it was time for us to meet his French counterpart. He sent him a telegram: *Two special stew friends, Trudy Baker and Rachel Jones, arrive tomorrow evening Orly 0600 hours. Please meet and care for. As ever. George.*

Pierre sent a telegram back to George: *Oui. Will provide special escort for Jones et Baker. Pierre.* What Pierre didn't tell George was that he'd received similiar telegrams the same day from a stew bum in Stockholm and a stew bum in Tel Aviv. Pierre answered them, too, promising special escort for their favorite stewardesses. Naturally, that put Pierre in a bit of a tight spot for the evening. But he was known as an inventive and flexible young Frenchman. One of the great, all-time stew bums, you might say.

While we were winging towards Paris that night, elaborate plans were being laid for handling all six stews the same night, plans that were explained to us during that chance meeting in the coffee shop. Pierre was reluctant to talk about it, but after much cajoling and kidding, he told us how he planned to accommodate all of us without letting anyone know of the other pairs of stews.

When Pierre dragged Henri into the scheme, Henri made a perfectly reasonable suggestion.

"Iz simple, Pierre," he said. "You take zem all to dinner and make ze party of it. Oui?"

"No, Henri. It is important that each feels that Pierre cares only for her . . . or in this case, them. Besides, you know how Pierre enjoys his little romps in ze sack, Oui? With *six* of them, it is a good chance that Pierre will make love with *one* of them."

Henri understood. He asked if he, too, could attempt to woo one of us. Pierre was hesitant, but agreed that Henri could take his chances as long as he didn't interfere with Pierre's evening. Henri promised. Actually, it was no act of generosity on Pierre's part. Henri was hardly what you would term an attractive male. In fact, he was more aptly described as gross and offensive. But he was loyal to Pierre, and that's what Pierre needed more than anything that night—loyalty—plus a willingness to follow instructions.

We almost didn't get to meet Pierre on arrival at Orly Field. We arrived on time, waited thirty minutes then decided to head for the hotel without him. We climbed into a waiting cab and gave the driver the name of our hotel. He was pulling away from the curb when a young Frenchman, replete with waxed moustache, long hair and flowing scarf leaped in front of the cab.

"Halte!" the young man commanded. It was either run him over or stop so the driver jammed on the brakes, tossing our luggage all over the cab. The young man clenched his fist at the driver and yelled a few French obscenities. The driver yelled back, threw the cab in low gear again and gunned the engine. The young man leaped back onto the curb, slammed his fist on the cab's hood and came back to Trudy's side.

"Is Trudy *et* Rachel?" he asked.

"Yes," Trudy answered. The driver started to pull away again but we shouted for him to stop. He did, and started swearing at us, which only made the young man outside the window madder.

"I am Pierre," the young man announced. "Pierre Popinjois, *ami* of George Kelman."

"Oh, hi, Pierre. I'm Trudy and this is Rachel."

"Oui. And welcome to Pareeee."

Traffic was building up behind us by this time and

horns were tooting frantically. The driver kept yelling at us in French, waving his hands and occasionally thumping one against his head.

"I have a car," Pierre said, opening Trudy's door. "Come." That really did the driver in. He leaped out of the cab and ran around it after Pierre. They stood nose-to-nose in a Gallic temper tantrum. Finally, Pierre reached into his pocket and pulled out some money which he slammed into the driver's outstretched hand. We dragged our luggage out of the cab, smiled at the driver and walked off with Pierre. He led us to a parking lot in which his Citroen, not one of the fancy models that goes "whooooooosh" whenever the engine is started or stopped, but the model that looks like a tin can of cat food, was parked. We left Orly and Pierre drove like a Steve McQueen chase scene. We flew in and out of Paris, Pierre's one hand on the horn, his other hand out the window shaking at fellow-stunt men.

"We're in no rush, Pierre," I gasped.

"Oui." He pushed harder on the accelerator. Moments later—or it just seemed that way—we were in downtown Paris. It was alive and vivacious. We pulled up in front of the D'lena Hotel, a popular hotel with airline crews. Pierre hopped out, grabbed our bags, stiff-armed a bellhop and led us to the desk. He obtained our room key, took us up in the elevator which threatened an asthmatic breakdown at any moment and led us to our room. It was very old-fashioned and pleasant. Pierre checked his watch once we were inside the room. 7:01.

"Tres bien, oui?"

"It's great, Pierre. Very nice."

"Oui. Now, Pierre would suggest you take a bath and a nap so you will be clean and rested for ze big night with Pierre."

"Gee, I'm not at all tired," Trudy said. I was about to defend the state of my bodily cleanliness when Pierre made his suggestion more forceful.

"No, no, no, no, no," he said, shaking his head back and forth and checking his watch. "Believe in Pierre when he say that to see Pierre's Pareeee at night ze rest and bath are important. Oui?"

Arguing seemed futile. We could have just gone out on our own but that would have offended Pierre and, probably, George. So we relented and agreed to bathe and rest.

"Good. I will be back at eight thirty and we will go to Pierre's favorite restaurant in all Pareeee. *Au revoir.*" He backed from the room, throwing kisses all the way.

Little did we know, as we called the desk to arrange for a key to the shower room, that Pierre was running down the fire stairs, through the lobby and out to the alley that ran alongside the hotel. He jumped into the Ford Mustang that was parked there, an old model with thousands of creases and dents. Behind the wheel sat Henri. Maybe at this point we should describe Henri for you. He's fat, very fat. We never saw him wear anything but an Hawaiian sportshirt and dirty chino pants. Broken sandals flopped from dirty feet. His hair was matted and dirty. And he never seemed to be without a peach or an orange or an apple. Watching him suck on a piece of fruit was like watching passengers try to eat soup in turbulence; most of it goes down the chin and onto the clothing.

"Well, Henri?" Pierre said, settling back in the seat and lighting a cigarette. "Did all go well with ze stewardesses from SAS?"

"Oui, Pierre," Henri answered. "I pick up ze stewardesses and drive zem here, just like you say to do, Pierre."

"They are in their rooms, Henri?"

"Oui, Pierre. I tell zem to take ze bath and ze nap, just like you say to do, Pierre."

"You tell them you are business associate to Pierre? They believe you, Henri?"

"No, Pierre. I tell zem I am ze chauffeur of Pierre. Zey believe zat."

"O.K." Pierre contemplated the situation for a few moments. "You know, Henri. I think maybe I should have taken ze Mustang to meet ze American stews. They did not seem to like ze Citroen."

"Oui, Pierre. Ze Swedish girls did not seem to like ze Mustang, eizer. Zay start riding in the front seat wiz me, but zen zay move to ze back seat."

Pierre suggested that the girls moved because Henri smelled.

"How many times have I told you to take ze bath, Henri?"

"Many times, Pierre."

Pierre checked his watch. 7:17.

"It is time for you to pick up ze other stewardesses at the airport, Henri."

"More stewardesses, Pierre?"

"Oui, Henri, ze ones from El Al. Lester Hondel, mon ami in Tel Aviv, sent me ze cable. They arrive at 8:15. Take ze Mustang. You know Jooooooosh girls like ze bigger cars, Henri."

"How would I know that, Pierre? I am not Jooooooosh."

"Maybe you should read some Jooooosh books, Henri. Some books like ze Complaint of Portnoy."

"Is Jooooooosh?"

"Oui. Now hurry, Henri, pick up ze girls from El Al. Bring them to ze hotel and tell them to take a bath and nap and be ready for dinner at eleven."

Henri went to Orly to pick up the girls from Tel Aviv. Pierre came into the hotel lobby and called us

on the house phone. He told us he was involved in a
last minute business deal and would be late. "Henri,
my chauffeur, will pick you up at nine and take you
to ze restaurant. I will join you there."

While we laid back on our beds and waited for
nine, Pierre, after hanging up, went to the men's room
and washed his face and combed his hair. Then he
took the elevator up to the room occupied by the two
stews from SAS.

"Who are you?" one of the busty blonde beauties
asked him.

"I am Pierre, *ami* of Nils Olsen in Stockholm."

"Ja. Come in." Pierre entered the room in time to
catch the other SAS gal pick up a towel and drape
it around a very ample and nude body. Pierre watched
with intense interest as the girl dressed behind a flimsy
screen. In an instant he'd made up his mind that she
was the one he'd most like to share his bed with that
night . . . although he wasn't boxing himself in at that
early stage. When both SAS girls were dressed, Pierre
led them through the lobby and into his Citroen.

"I am taking you to ze favorite restaurant of
Pierre," he told them. "It is ze best in Pareeee." He
took them to Chez Michel, a moderately priced place
with large portions.

While we continued our nap in our clean bodies,
and Pierre ordered drinks for himself and the SAS
girls, Henri was approaching the El Al girls at Orly.
They didn't want to go with him because of the way
he looked, but he invoked Pierre's name often enough
to persuade them. They got in front of the Mustang
with Henri but soon asked for him to stop so they
could ride in back. He shrugged and sucked away on
his peach all the way back to Paris.

Henri checked the El Al gals into the hotel, told
them Pierre would pick them up at eleven and headed
for our room. I answered his knock.

"Bonne nuit," the chubby little man with body odor said.

"Who are you?" I demanded.

"I am Henri, ze associate of Pierre. He tell me to take you to ze restaurant and he will meet us zere." He looked at Trudy who was surveying him with disgust. Henri looked down to check that his pants weren't open. Trudy followed his hands which led Henri to believe she was interested in his lower anatomy. He confessed to Pierre later in the evening that he was certain Trudy was the most willing of all the girls that night. Pierre, in turn, confessed this to us at the coffee shop counter the next night. But that's getting ahead of the story. We went with Henri to the restaurant. The owner sat us at a table and we all sat looking at each other. No one said anything. Henri started biting his nails and ran his greasy hand through his greasy hair a number of times.

"I'd like a drink," Trudy said.

"Oui." Henri ordered the drinks and excused himself. We assumed he went to the men's room. But what he did was go to the phone and call Pierre at Chez Michel.

"Ze American girls are having ze drink wiz me at La Grille, Pierre. What does Henri do now?"

Pierre checked his watch. It was, by that time, ten o'clock. He instructed Henri to have us order dinner and to tell us Pierre would join us shortly. Then, Henri was to go back to the hotel and take the El Al girls to another restaurant."

"Which restaurant?" Henri asked Pierre.

"Any one. Look on ze list I give you."

"Pierre."

"Oui, Henri?"

"I am getting tired, Pierre. Besides, zese American girls do not like me. Ze make faces at Henri."

"Of course, Henri. Maybe if you would buy ze bar

of soap . . ." Pierre lectured Henri for a few minutes and hung up.

Pierre was reluctant to leave Chez Michel and the two SAS stews. Olga made it clear she liked Pierre by reaching under the table and squeezing his thigh a few times. He allowed his foot to nuzzle up against her legs and it was all going beautifully for Pierre, too beautifully to run out now. Besides, he even began to feel that the other girl, Vera, was also taking an active interest in him. This led Pierre to envision his wildest dreams coming true, a stewardess orgy, with Swedish girls, yet. He'd heard of it happening with other stew bums in other countries, but it had never happened yet for Pierre. Maybe tonight was the night.

Henri came back to our table and told us he had to leave. He handed us menus and called for a waiter.

"Where's Pierre?" Trudy demanded, fed up with the game by now.

"What?" Henri asked, his face taking on a confused and defensive expression.

"Pierre. I want Pierre now," Trudy said with much authority.

"Is coming later, Pierre is."

"Call him," Trudy demanded.

Henri shrugged. He went to the phone and called Pierre.

"What is it now, Henri?" Pierre asked, annoyed at another intrusion.

"Is something good, Pierre. One of ze American girls, Trudy, wants you. She says she wants you *now*. I watch her closely in ze hotel room and I am sure she has . . . what you call in English? . . . hot pants?"

"Is true, Henri?"

"Oui. Is in heat, like a dog, Pierre."

"Oui. I will come."

Pierre hung up and squeezed his hands together in delight. Two Swedish girls and one American girl . . .

together. He could see it all, the very big bed, the Swedes saying "Ja" to everything, the American girl saying "Yes" to all his requests. But Pierre started to wonder whether an American girl would agree to that kind of group fun with the Swedish girls. Pierre reviewed the situation. America and Sweden were on good terms. But there was the recent problem of American military defectors finding sanctuary in Sweden. Pierre decided to come to see us and take a first-hand look at Trudy in her supposed state of need. He'd leave Vera and Olga alone for awhile, explaining he'd just received an urgent phone call from a business associate. He felt he had things under enough control to leave them for an hour. He begged their forgiveness and they gave him sad but compassionate looks. He kissed them goodbye and backed from the table, uttering little French phrases of love and adoration. He jumped in his Citroen and raced to La Grille where we were into our appetizer—*Gratin de langoustines.*

Pierre joined us just about the time Henri knocked on the El Al girls' door. One of them opened it and let out a grunt upon seeing Henri. He tried to step into the room but she slammed the door on his foot. He howled and pleaded with her to listen to him. He assured them he was there at Pierre's request and that he was to take them to a restaurant where Pierre would shortly join them. The girls held a conference in Hebrew and decided they would go with "the pig" and wait for Pierre. Henri was pleased. He clasped his hand to his heart and followed them to the elevator.

"What restaurant are we going to?" one of the girls asked.

Henri had run through a mental list of Pierre's favorites and, in a moment of sheer creative thought, decided the girls from El Al would appreciate a Jewish restaurant.

"Goldberg's," Henri answered. "On Rue des Ro-
siers."

"GOLDBERG'S?"

"Oui. Is best Jooooosh food in Pareeee."

"We don't want Jewish food in Paris. We can get
all the Jewish food we want in . . ."

"Oui, I know," Henri interrupted. "In Tel Aviv."

"No, in New York."

"But ze menu is in French. Please, sweet girls, zis
is ze place Pierre has chosen. Please no fight wiz
Henri."

Everyone piled into the Mustang and went to Goldberg's. One of the girls began laughing at the whole
situation. Here they were, in Paris for the night and
they end up having dinner in a Jewish restaurant
with a fat Frenchman who hadn't bathed in three
months. Henri laughed, too, but he knew there was a
bitter edge to the laughter. He grabbed the menu,
summoned the waiter and ordered loudly. *"Pain
azyme, saumon fumé, foie hache et trois poisson farci,
s'il vous plaît."*

The waiter poked his head through the kitchen door
and yelled, "One order matzos, three salmon specials,
a bowl 'a chopped liver and three gefilte fish."

"Toda raba," Henri yelled to the waiter.

"L'hayim," the waiter responded.

"You thanked him in Hebrew," the girls said to
Henri.

"Oui," Pierre answered sheepishly. "I am French,
but I am also ze Jooo. Ze French Jooo is what Henri is."

The girls warmed to the fat little man across from
them. They asked about his family and he told them
he still had relatives in Israel, although he didn't know
very much about them.

"Where?" the girls asked.

"Givatayim."

"That's amazing, Henri. We have relatives in Givatayim."

"Oui? Who are ze?"

"Rubin. The Rubin family."

Henri leaped up and clapped his hands. "Is my relatives, too." From that moment on, Henri and the El Al girls got along wonderfully. They ate and drank and laughed and had the best time Henri could remember in years.

For us, it wasn't such a great time, although Trudy had taken steps to turn the evening into something more pleasant. Just before Pierre arrived, she'd placed a call to Marvin Sweetheart, our flight's captain. She suggested he grab Marty Sims, the first officer, and we'd all paint Paris red. Sweetheart was agreeable and promised to meet us at La Grille in a half hour. Pierre didn't know anything of these plans as he sat at the table and whispered sweet little words in Trudy's ear. "Aah, my love, my dream. Pierre comes running like ze bull when he hears he is wanted." He started kissing Trudy's hand and made it to her elbow before she yanked her arm away.

"I offend you, ma chérie. Pardon. It is just that your loveliness sweeps Pierre off his unworthy feet."

Trudy giggled.

"Please excuse Pierre's forcefulness, chérie. Let us turn our conversation to more practical matters of ze world. Tell me, it is true in America no one likes ze Swedish people because ze American soldiers go hide in Sweden?"

"That's not true at all," I said.

Pierre gave out one of those gutteral Maurice Chevalier laughs and started kissing Trudy's arm again, picking up where he left off. He was past the elbow and heading for the shoulder and neck when Captain Sweetheart and Marty Sims entered the restaurant. Sweetheart was wearing his olive green suit and ten-gallon cowboy hat.

"Howdy Trudy. What say, Rach?"

"Who are these men?" Pierre demanded.

"Our leaders," I answered.

"Leaders?"

"Oui, Pierre." We introduced him to our flight crew, thanked him for the dinner, paid our own tab and left the restaurant with Sweetheart and Sims. We hailed a cab and were climbing into it when we saw Pierre come racing out of La Grille and jump into his Citroen. We waved as he pulled away from the curb.

"Wonder what he'll do for the rest of the night," Trudy mused.

"Probably go home and drown his sorrow in wine," I offered.

We didn't know then that Pierre was racing back to Chez Michel where he assumed Olga and Vera would be waiting anxiously. He arrived just in time to see them walking arm-in-arm with two elderly French gentlemen.

"Olga, Vera. Is Pierre."

Olga came over to the Citroen and explained the men were long-lost uncles who happened to come into Chez Michel. "We are so sorry, Pierre, but family matters must come first. The next time we are in Paris —and you aren't so busy—we'll spend an evening with you." She walked away and joined Vera and their uncles.

Pierre beat his fists against the steering wheel. Then he remembered. El Al. Maybe it wasn't too late. He reviewed his list of restaurants. The last place Henri would take two Jewish airline stewardesses from Tel Aviv would be to a Jewish restaurant in Paris. He drove off and checked every place he could think of. No luck. Finally, he went to Goldberg's. The owner gave him a hug and handed him a note. It was from Henri.

> Pierre—I tell you I am not Jewish. Is not true.
> In fact, girls from El Al are cousins. I take them

to visit other cousin they no know in Rouen. I
return Mustang in morning.

Henri

Trudy and I carefully nursed a hangover the next
morning. We took the airport limo late that afternoon
for Orly, our eyes on the low, gray clouds and ground
fog that seemed to sweep in and blanket Paris. Operations informed us that all flights were cancelled, and
that the weather would probably hold that way until
later that night.

"I'm starved," I said. "Let's grab a sandwich."

We went to the coffee shop, ordered, and fell into
a light conversation with two SAS stews and two El
Al stews. As we drank coffee, the conversation turned
to more weighty matters like men . . . Frenchmen
in particular. We mentioned Pierre, and that started
it. We swapped stories about the previous evening
and the more we told, the harder we laughed. Of
course, there were certain gaps in our knowledge of
the evening and we assumed they would never be
filled in. But then we heard a clatter at the door and
saw Pierre and Henri come bumbling through. They
did a marvelous double-take when they saw us all
sitting together. Pierre admitted they had come to the
airport in the hope of salvaging something of the
fiasco for Pierre. After much cajoling and joking,
Pierre was persuaded to tell all. He did, and the
gaps were filled.

George Kelman asked us how we enjoyed Paris and
Pierre when we returned home to New York.

"Wonderful, George. A wonderful city and a fine
young man."

"Good," he said. "He has a fine reputation all over
the world."

"He deserves it," I answered.

CHAPTER IV

"Lucky Lucy"

"A loser is . . ."

Lucy Cordish was a loser. There aren't many people who are losers in all things, but Lucy was one of those exceptions. There was virtually nothing in Lucy's life that ended up better than when she started out, although becoming a stewardess did loom large as the great "win" of her 23 years.

Everyone liked Lucy, which should count as some sort of success. But Lucy didn't know everyone liked her, so this, too, was but another entry in her loss column. Our fondness for Lucy wasn't without reservations. In any given month in which you were assigned to work with her, you could count on an unlikely number of delays, a disproportionate amount of clear-air turbulence, a number of airsick passengers above which was usually experienced in one month and a ratio of children to adults that was always higher than usual.

Still, Lucy Cordish was a good kid, depressed most of the time, but always willing to take a fling at whatever you suggested as a remedy for her loser psychology. The last time we remember Lucy trying a remedy was during one glorious night at the Place du Casino in Monte Carlo, the glamorous city on the Riviera of Monaco. We'd worked one of those infernal puddle-jumping flights that started in New York, went to Paris, Geneva, Rome, and eventually dumped us in Genoa. We'd worked a deal with some other stews to swap trips, giving us a few days to rent a car and motor down to Monaco and the lovely area surrounding that jewel on the Mediterranean. We persuaded Lucy to come with us, but only after we promised to forget about her once we got to Monaco.

"The last person you want with you when you're gambling is me," she said with a tear in her voice. We told her we were only going to bet a few dollars just for the fun of it. But Lucy was vehement about splitting up. We agreed, rented the car, and set out along the southern coast of France.

We arrived in Monte Carlo at six in the evening, checked into a marvelous hotel right on the beach, dressed and set out for dinner and a night on the town.

"I'll just stay here and read a book," Lucy said.

"No you won't," I answered. "You're coming with us."

"Well, just for dinner."

We dined on *beignets des moules,* mussels dipped in batter, at a charming restaurant called Bec Rouge. None of us particularly enjoyed our meal, but the waiter insisted we have this speciality of the house and we didn't want to offend him. Besides, he was just as cute as could be, and Trudy had taken a definite liking to him. He knew it, and kept hovering over her saying little French things, smiling and gazing at her with bedroom eyes.

"I wish he'd asked me out," Trudy said as we were getting in the car to head for the casino.

"He would have if I wasn't there," Lucky Lucy said mournfully; she was slipping into one of her deeper depressions. "Just take me back to the hotel and I'll read a book or drown myself in the ocean."

"You'll do nothing of the kind, Lucy. You're coming with us and gamble a few dollars. Maybe that's just what you need to make you feel like a winner." We'd gone through this kind of thing before with Lucy. You just had to keep insisting and telling her everything would be all right.

We arrived at the Casino at about nine, gave the
car to one of the young men in front (who also
seemed to take a shine to Trudy, much to her pleasure and to my annoyance at being slighted by the
handsome young men of the area. Only rich old men
seemed to turn around and look at me.) We walked
through the huge doors and into the lavish lobby of
the Casino. Directly in front of us stood the doors
of the Foyer de la Danse, a theatre within the Casino
from which the audience flows during intermissions
for a quick crack at the gambling tables. We turned
left and walked to the doors leading to the main gambling room, a very large but surprisingly shabby room
in which hundreds of people were milling about from
game table to game table in search of some action and,
hopefully, some winnings.

"I'll just find a chair in the corner and wait for
you," Lucy said.

"No, Lucy. You come with us." We walked over
to the roulette table and stood behind the players. A
few of the men and women were dressed in evening
wear, but most looked like middle-class wage earners
out for an evening of poker. We were attracted to that
particular table because there seemed to be a great
deal of joyous noise coming from the people surrounding it. Obviously, some substantial winning was
taking place.

We watched the next spin of the roulette wheel.
It came up 11-black. No one had anything on 11-
black. Again the wheel was turned by the croupier
. . . 3-red. Again, no winner. Someone started to
grumble about the table's good luck changing. Someone else agreed. And Lucy walked away.

"That dope," I said, heading after her.

"No, Rachel," Trudy said, grabbing my arm. "Let
her go. She really believes she changed the luck at the
table. Besides, sometimes I get sick of playing games
with Lucky Lucy. Come on. Let's gamble a little."

We got our chips, looked around for Lucy, couldn't
see her, and went back to the roulette table. The luck
seemed to have changed a bit, and we started placing
a few small wagers. We won on our first bets, which
led Trudy to suggest that maybe Lucy was, in fact,
a bad luck carrier to be avoided when engaging in
games of chance. But that's not what Count Alexis
Cord Ashbrush was evidently thinking when he spotted
Lucy sitting on a Victorian chair in the lobby. He
came over to her and struck up a conversation. We
noticed them from the casino and decided to go out
and see what kind of luck she was having this time.
She introduced us to the Count, and to see them
together would make you believe it was the ultimate
meeting of the world's top loser and greatest winner.
The Count looked successful, in fact, downright rich.
And there sat Lucy, eyes to the floor, fingers twirling
nervously and a constant frog in her throat which
made all her answers to everything come out weary
and resigned.

But as we stood and talked, we began to notice
some discrepancies in the Count's appearance. The
heels on his patent leather shoes were run down. His
shirt, one of those pleated formal affairs, had suffered
too many washings with strong detergents, or too many
poundings on the riverbank. And his fingernails were
rough and dirty. Lucy didn't seem to notice any of
these things. All she saw was this handsome, impressive *winner*. And he was talking to her without suffering any visible bad luck.

"I have asked Miss Cordish if she would accompany
me for a drive in the moonlight," the Count said
to us.

"That sounds wonderful, Lucy," Trudy said with a
big smile.

"It is a pleasant evening," the Count continued. "It
is unfortunate that my automobile is being repaired.

It is the problem with the Rolls Royce. Such good manufacturing but so difficult to find competent people for repairing it."

"I know what you mean," Lucy said. "I once had a Volkswagen and when I took it in for a grease and oil change, the garage caught fire and the car was destroyed. I forgot to renew my insurance so I lost it all. I was going to buy another car but I just knew it would happen again."

The Count looked very sympathetic. "Yes, my dear. We will hire a taxi and have the driver take us for a leisurely tour. I would suggest my yacht for a sail but I allowed good friends to take it for a week along the Coast."

Lucy understood. We glanced at each other and grappled with the temptation to break it up and save Lucy from an evening with this phoney. But it was obviously none of our business, and besides, he wasn't that bad a fellow. Phoney, yes, but likeable. We could only guess Lucy's thoughts at the moment. She seemed to be in a dreamy fog in which she knew she would have an affair with this man, probably with the winner taking all. But what could a loser do? Losers were there for winners to take.

We went back to the gambling tables; the bloom was off our luck. We lost what we'd won previously and headed back to the hotel.

We knocked on Lucy's door but there was no answer. We put our ears to it and could hear no heavy breathing, sighing or crying. We asked discreetly at the desk if Madame in 12A had returned yet and just as discreetly we were told that they would be glad to leave a note for Madame in her box. We went to sleep lulled by the insinuating sound of the surf.

I was awakened at an ungodly hour in the morning. Trudy was shaking me and laughing hysterically and holding a note under my nose. She had found it under the door. It said, "Thanks, girls, for making me change my luck. Wake me as soon as you find this. Love, Lucy."

We grabbed our robes and tripped down the stairs to 12A. We banged on the door and banged some more and were about to give up when an ecstatic Lucy flung open the door. She stood there naked like something out of a Swedish movie. Absolutely beaming.

"Let's go to Grasse and buy perfume today," Lucy began. "Let's buy quarts of it."

"All right," I said lamely. "Let's."

"I've got a thousand dollars I didn't have yesterday," Lucy exploded.

"A thousand dollars?" Trudy said. "What did you have to do for it?"

By that time Lucy had come off her high at least to the point of wrapping a sheet around her. She stood there looking like Brigitte Bardot on one of her best mornings.

"Count Alexis gave it to me," Lucy replied mysteriously. "For bringing him luck."

We were stunned. Ecstatic but stunned, waiting for details. Lucy filled us in. She had finally noticed his ravelled shirt and worn heels but she went with him because she felt he was a loser, too. She knew all his talk about a Rolls and a yacht were lies. And she couldn't have been less surprised when he turned out to have holes in his socks and patches in his slip.

"His slip?"

"Actually he pronounces it sleep. It's French for what we call jockey shorts. You know, bikini underwear."

"No, I didn't know," I admitted. "And when and where did you get to see his 'sleep?' "

"We came back here," Lucy said romantically.

"We asked for you downstairs and they lied beautifully," I said.

"That's what's so great about European hotels. Everybody seems to want to play Cupid."

"Is he married?" Trudy wanted to know.

"Who knows?" Lucy said. "All I do know is that he was warm and tender and very European in bed. At least I think the things he did were European. Anyway, it was nice."

"I'm sure it was," Trudy suggested.

"There was only one sticky thing about it. I don't think the poor man had had a bath in days. But I opened the shutters and then it wasn't too bad. We both took showers before we went back to the Casino."

"That's nice," Trudy said. "What time was that? We didn't see you."

"Who knows?" said Lucy blithely. "Quite late. After the theatre. You know that five hundred francs I had. He wouldn't let me play it. I told him everything about myself. I told him my whole life story as a loser."

"Why?" Trudy wanted to know.

"I couldn't help it. He was pretending to have all the money in the world and I knew he probably didn't have a place to hang his hat. Anyway, we got some chips and we played."

"What number did you play?"

"Well, first he insisted I put my hand in his pocket. For luck."

"Which, of course, you did."

"Of course. I didn't want to do it . . . pick the number, that is. But I did. I really did."

Then, in breathless sentences, she told us how he had turned his meager supply of chips into winnings of over two thousand dollars.

"He absolutely insisted on giving me half. I almost died when he counted out the money. He gave it all to me in fifty-dollar bills. Twenty of them. Just look," she screamed excitedly, reaching for her puse.

"If you two make such an unbeatable twosome, why

not try it again? We'll go buy the perfume. You stick with the Count."

"No," Lucy said, still looking for her purse. "Our luck wouldn't last. We both know that. It was one wonderful night. Now it's over."

Lucy was tearing around the bedroom now, fishing through her suitcase, looking under the bed. "I'm so excited, I must have mislaid my evening bag," she said calmly going on with her romantic saga. "After he made me take the money, he put me in a cab. He kissed me ever so lightly and told me this had been the most beautiful night of his life."

"You came straight home?"

"Of course," said Lucy. "When I got out of the cab, I was like, you know, in a daze. I wanted to wake you up and talk to you but I knew you were sleeping. So I stopped at the desk and wrote a note." She stopped. "Omigod," said Lucy, "when I wrote that note I didn't have my purse with me. Omigod. I lost it. I lost it. I left it in the cab."

I wanted to go straight to Prince Rainier. There couldn't be more than twenty cabs in the entire principality. It shouldn't take the police more than half an hour to discover which taxi had dropped Lucy at our hotel, leaving behind a small beige evening purse with a Saks label in it, some Kleenex, a comb, a lipstick and twenty fifty-dollar bills.

But Lucy had lapsed into a catatonic state. She had been a winner for one night. She had bloomed last night and faded in the morning. Now she was a loser again.

"I warned you not to hang out with me," she said.

We never got to spend a leisurely day in Nice, we never visited Eze on the rocks. We never took that drive into the hills behind Cannes to the perfume center at Grasse. We checked out of the hotel and flew back to New York that night. It was an uneventful trip except for one baby throwing up on Lucy.

CHAPTER V

"*I Am Curious:*
Red White and Blue"

"Who wants to go to Copenhagen?" I asked Trudy and our dates as we sat sipping wine. It wasn't an offer I was making. It was asked with a certain note of disgust.

"Me, me," Trudy's date responded, a big smile on his face.

"Watch him, Trudy. He's a sex maniac," I said.

"I am not. It has nothing to do with all those gorgeous Danish girls and the free thinking they practice and the sex. I'm interested in going to Copenhagen because of the . . . the . . . the gorgeous Danish girls and the free thinking and the sex. You're right. I am a sex maniac. Let's go to my place, Trudy."

We discussed all the obvious reasons why men want to go to Denmark and Sweden, which proved the point I was making when I asked my question. Trudy and I had received our July assignment. It was New York-Copenhagen, and neither of us looked forward to it. We were simply being honest; stewardesses fly looking for eligible men. Scandinavia seemed to offer little more for us then a month's competition with a Danish national resource—beautiful girls. Who needed it?

We managed to get rid of our dates early despite their protestations at being sloughed off after an expensive dinner. Both fellows had spent the afternoon at their hair stylist and looked like identical Ken dolls with cement hair. Both wore double-breasted suits, wide, flowered ties and striped shirts with very large collars. We'd met them while shopping that morning in Bloomingdale's and, being at liberty that evening, took them up on their dinner offer. It was all very dull, and we were both very pleased when they grumbled farewells at our door and presumably set out for a fast fling at the East Side singles joints in search of something to cap off their evening. We curled up in our beds and watched an old movie, saying little to each other and contemplating our Copenhagen assignment, which would start at eight the next morning when we took off from Kennedy Airport for the Land of the Midnight Sun.

"Do you know anything at all about Copenhagen?" I asked Trudy.

"Nope. Just what I hear."

"What do you hear?"

"Well, I hear there's a lot of sex going on and they love dirty books and movies and have canals and stuff like that."

I fell asleep and dreamed I was walking down the main street in Copenhagen. The streets were lined with thousands of blonde girls in bikinis, and each girl had a forty inch bust and a face out of a magazine and they were all laughing at me as I walked along. Then I looked down and saw I wasn't wearing any clothes and I ran around trying to find something to put on and they all kept laughing and pointing and . . . I woke up in a cold sweat. "Trudy," I yelled.

"What?" I'd woken her up.

"Have you been dreaming?"

"Yes, dammit, and I'd like to finish it."

"What were you dreaming about?"

"I was dreaming about my date tonight. I was luring him into bed. He said he'd love to, but he'd forgotten his hair net and the stylist wasn't open on Sunday so he didn't want to mess it up."

"What do you want to finish *that* dream for?"

"Because I was about to grab him by the hair and really ruffle it all up and watch him cry. Now shut up and go back to sleep." I tried, but couldn't get the dream out of my head.

"Trudy," I whispered.

"What?"

"Do you think they'll laugh at us?"

"Who?"

"The Danish girls?"

Trudy didn't bother answering. She looked at the clock, saw it was six A.M., got up, showered, dressed and was ready to leave for the airport by 6:45. She hadn't said a word to me and made it plain she was angry at my foolish questioning in the middle of the night. We left the apartment, hailed a cab and rode to Kennedy in silence. By the time we passed under the entrance signs to the airport, I'd forgotten about my phobia. Trudy seemed to be thawing a little and even tried to make small talk with our driver, a burly gentleman from The Bronx named Herman Glotz—Hack Number 30604.

"Bet you hate getting a fare out here at this hour," Trudy said to him.

"Yeah, dat's usually true. But not if yah know what's doin', like me. I'll drop youse off and head over tah SAS. They got a flight gits in from Copenhagen about now and youse can always git a fare with one 'a them Danish broads. Man, like I love my old lady and all dat, but them Danes and Swedes is somethin' else. Boy oh boy, I seen a Danish stewardess de other day'd make Anita Ekberg look like Little Red Ridin' Hood. Dey just got it all over da American goils." Mr. Glotz sighed, pulled up in front of our terminal and accepted our tip with a mumble. I didn't want to tip him anything, but Trudy insisted.

"Good luck finding one of them Danish girls," Trudy said as we slammed the door.

"Yeah. Dey got generosity, too. Not like American broads." He shoved the accelerator to the floor and

roared away from the loading ramp. I looked after
him and cursed. My dream loomed large again as we
signed in and boarded our aircraft for the pre-flight
check.

"Who's the new stew?" I asked our flight engineer.
We'd noticed her board the aircraft a few moments
before.

"Name's Inga," he answered. "Inga Petersen. Nice
looking girl, huh? Somebody told me she was Miss
Sweden or something a few years ago. Maybe it was
Miss Denmark. Anyway, she's a doll."

He was right. Inga Petersen was a doll. She was
very blonde and tall and buxom, and I wanted to kick
her in the shins when we were introduced.

"We understand you were Miss Denmark," Trudy
said as we settled into the jump seats for take-off.

"No," Inga smiled, "I could never be Miss Denmark.
There are too many beautiful girls in my country. I
was Miss Odense. That is the little town where Hans
Christian Andersen was born. There are not too many
pretty girls there, so I could win."

By the time we were airborne and winging towards
Copenhagen, I'd slipped to a new point in morale. All
I wanted to do was go back to Bloomingdale's and
enjoy a few admiring glances from the Saturday crowd.
Miss Odense went about her duties in the cabin with
all the confidence and grace of the world's biggest winner. Every male on the flight, with the exception of one
nervous fellow with a hatchet-faced wife, was infatu-
ated with Inga and her good looks. The only passengers who seemed to vie for my attention were four
little kids traveling with their parents. They adored
me.

The trip was uneventful and we arrived at Copenhagen right on schedule. We checked into the Dan
Hotel, a new structure near the airport where airline
crews stayed, and met for a drink a few hours later

at the hotel bar. Trudy had invited Inga to join us and she, in turn, had invited a former boyfriend. Before he arrived, Inga told us a little about him.

"Have you heard of Ollie Borehol?" she asked.

"No."

"I used to go on dates when Ollie was a freshman at the State School of Arts. Then I began flying and did not see Ollie any more. But then I heard he was making motion pictures and was being very successful here in Denmark. I haven't seen him in more than a year."

Ollie Borehol arrived moments later. He was very short and fat, sported hair below his shoulders, a moustache that rivaled his hair, and wore zebra pants and jacket. The jacket hung open revealing a pale, flabby chest with a tiny tuft of blond hair that sort of curled up in a corkscrew and pointed out at whomever he was facing. He immediately embraced Inga and gave her a passionate kiss. She introduced us to him and he gave us each a hug and kiss, although our stiffness precluded any passion in the act.

Ollie ordered a round of aquavit, or snaps, as it's called in Denmark, a deceivingly light-colored liquor with the kick of a mule, and launched into a discourse on life, love and his career in films.

"My first film was ten minutes long, but in that time I gave the world a message to be remembered. Maybe you saw it at a festival in New York. It was called *Haarklipning*."

"I don't remember any film by that name," I said.

"Perhaps you remember the message," Ollie said.

"What was the message?" I asked.

"It told of the loss of the individual in our society. It is why I named it *Haircut*."

"Is that what *haarklipning* means?"

"*Ja*. I photographed a haircut for ten minutes. With each strand of hair falling to the floor, the audience could feel the loss of the manhood, the individuality. For emphasis, the barber was a girl. She wore nothing. You see? You feel the power, the strength, the message?"

We assured Ollie we understood. He seemed pleased. He told us about other films, each a little longer and each enriching the world through its message. He was discussing his need for a new project when he suddenly jumped up from his Danish modern bar stool and grabbed Trudy by the shoulders. He shook her.

"Cut it out," Trudy said.

"No. I have inspiration for my new project. It is you, Trudy. It is you and your Americanism. It is you and your life in the sky. Will you be in my new film?" Inga was highly amused by the whole thing and sat giggling at the bar while Ollie worked his cinematic enthusiasm on Trudy. She looked over at me and I shrugged, indicating I really didn't have a thought on the subject.

"What do I have to do?" Trudy asked Ollie.

"Be what you are. Be an American stewardess. That is all I need." As an afterthought, he turned and assured me I was to be in the film, too. It was all so silly that I smiled and told him I'd love to be in his movie.

"Good. It is settled. When do you leave Copenhagen?"

"Tomorrow night."

"That's not much time. But I can do it. We will begin photography tomorrow morning at six. By tomorrow night, Ollie Borehol's next film will be ready for editing. And each of you will have carried another message to the world, a message of love and peace."

Ollie raced off on his bicycle in search of his angel and backer. Trudy and I caught a cab for downtown Copenhagen where we had a marvelous dinner at A Porta. We strolled through Tivoli Gardens and watched what seemed to be one million young couples embracing on benches, on street-corners and on the grass.

"They are affectionate, aren't they?" Trudy commented as we stopped and purchased two tiny porcelain objects as gifts for people back home.

"That's for sure. I've seen so much of it, I'm ready for a little affection myself." We didn't find any, although we did stroll along the boulevards of Copenhapen, stopped into a few student pubs, drank Tuborg beer, ate open-faced sandwiches and struck up a few conversations with handsome Danish college students who, it always ended up, were sitting waiting for their girlfriends to come back from the john. We returned to the hotel at midnight, discreetly looked the other way to avoid the night desk clerk who was locked in an embrace with an older Danish blonde lady and went to our room. There was a note tacked up on the door from Ollie: *"Trudy and Rachel. I have made the shooting schedule to begin at four A.M. to allow us to photograph some night scenes. Please be ready. Ollie.*

"The hell with you, Ollie," I mumbled, slipping into my shortie pajamas.

"Absolutely, Ollie," Trudy said in a Stan Laurel voice. "And good night."

At four A.M., we were shaken out of bed by a loud banging. Trudy grabbed a vase as a weapon and went to the door.

"Who is it?"

"Ollie. We're ready."

"Well, we're not ready. Go away and leave us alone."

"That's impossible. Everyone is here waiting to begin."

"Do it without us, Ollie."

"I cannot do it without you. It is about you. You must come."

"No."

The next voice was Inga's. "Please, Trudy and Rachel," she said. "Ollie has the whole crew here and there is a lot of money involved. Let me come in."

Trudy opened the door and Inga entered the room She was dressed very hip and had let her hair down to hang loose over her shoulders. She pleaded with us not to let Ollie down, especially in the light of the financing he'd received for the film. "In fact," she whispered, "the backer of the film is here with Ollie. He is a very powerful man in Denmark, one of our biggest publishers. Ollie is the first filmmaker in which he has taken an interest and this is very important to Ollie. Please do not disappoint him. Please."

"OK."

Inga went to the door, opened it and everyone came in. There was Ollie, dressed this time in pink dungarees, a fur vest and nothing else. He was followed by a portly gentleman, pink of cheek and well dressed. An assortment of young Danes came next, each a member of Ollie's film crew. There were probably six of them, although once this many people crowded into our room, it was hard to keep count. And then came the girls. Four of them. Each was right out of a Scandinavian travel booklet, with long, straight blonde hair, classic faces and dressed in various mod outfits. With Inga, the total came to thirteen, not including us.

Ollie gave me a big hug of welcome, which I considered a trifle forward considering I was still in my shortie pajamas. He turned to grab Trudy but she'd already made it into the bathroom.

"Come, come, come," Ollie said to me, wringing his hands. "Each minute we lose is much money lost. Get dressed and we go."

I turned around. Everyone was looking at me with silent, impatient faces. "But I can't get undressed in front of everyone." He threw his hands up in the air and turned to the portly man.

"Very strange," the backer said. "Strange."

I grabbed my clothes from the suitcase and backed to the bathroom door. It was locked. I knocked.

"Go away," Trudy said.

"It's me, Rachel. Open up and let me in."

Trudy unlatched the door and I slid through. Trudy hadn't gotten any further than getting out of her pajamas; she'd been standing nude in front of the mirror in a stupor. We started jabbering away about the whole situation and whether we should simply start yelling and toss everyone out when Ollie opened the door and stuck his head in. Trudy shrieked and threw a bar of soap at him. He managed to get the word hurry out before pulling his head back and closing the door. A minute later, Inga knocked. We let her in and she again pleaded with us to cooperate. "Mr. Kroner, the backer, likes you every much. He has great faith in Ollie, but is losing patience. Please, Rachel and Trudy, cooperate for Ollie's sake. Mr. Kroner has promised each of you a bonus if you help and work hard. He thinks you are very American-looking and very democratic. But he has a short temper."

We dressed and joined the crew in the room. Mr. Kroner beamed and took our hands. He had a very pronounced deodorant smell about him, but was pleasant enough. He led us out of the room, with Ollie and the rest following. Outside, we piled into cars and headed off towards the airport. My stomach grumbled and Ollie laughed. "Here," he said, handing us a paper bag. Inside were Danish rolls. We ate them with desperate gulps and sipped coffee from an army canteen which had been attached to Ollie's belt.

Our little caravan pulled into the main roadway of

Copenhagen's international airport and came to a stop in front of a maintenance hangar. We stumbled out in the dark and Ollie walked with us to the hangar door. "This is the opening of the film," he said as we reached the entrance. When I give the signal, you walk from here towards the camera which will be by the cars. Just walk and talk to yourselves. I will tell you when to stop." Ollie walked away. Two of the men in the crew held up flood lights and directed their light at us. Another crew member hoisted a camera on his shoulders and pointed it at us. Ollie signaled us to walk. We reached the camera and stopped. Everyone jumped in the cars and we headed back towards town.

"That's all we're doing here?" I asked, munching on another Danish.

"Yes. That establishes the theme of the film. You are two American airline stewardesses visiting Denmark. The darkness indicates to the audience that you are oppressed in matters of life and freedom of living. Now, we go to the major portion of the film. We will shoot it at the apartment of a friend. The message will now be clear."

Somehow, I felt I'd already gotten Ollie's message, but I dismissed my thoughts as being just another example of my hangup on Denmark. I should have followed my natural inclinations.

Dawn was breaking as we pulled up in front of an old apartment building near the center of Copenhagen. We walked up three flights of stairs, Ollie bringing us to a halt in front of an apartment door. It was painted purple, and featured a life-size poster of Sonny Tufts.

"Sonny Tufts? ? ? ?" I blurted out.

"Ja," Ollie said solemnly. "For many of the young people of Denmark, Mr. Tufts is a symbol of hope for the future."

Ollie knocked on Sonny's forehead and the door

was opened by a tall, handsome young man wearing a loin cloth and a smile. He was very well built.

"Ollie, my friend," the young man said, embracing our young filmmaker.

"Stud," Ollie responded, punching him in the belly a few times.

"Mr. Kroner," the tall young man said, reaching out and shaking Kroner's hand energetically.

"Stud Swensen," Kroner said with reverence. "It has been a long time since I have seen you. I believe the last time you worked for me was for that book jacket. Remember? The one with the cover of you, that blonde girl with the incredible cheekbones and the ape we rented from the zoo. Remember, Stud?"

"*Ja,* I remember well. I remember the girl when she told me she preferred the ape to me."

"Good cheekbones a brain does not make," Kroner said to soothe the memory.

We were introduced to Stud Swensen who, it turned out, was one of Denmark's leading male models. He appeared on many book jackets published by Mr. Kroner's publishing firm. It had been the largest publishing house in Denmark. Kroner told us about its demise while the crew set up the lights.

"Once, I was king of all life publishing in Denmark," he reflected, his eyes to the heavens.

"I didn't know *Life* was published here," Trudy said with wide-eyed innocence. "I have a cousin who works for *Life.* He fixes the computer when it mixes up the subscriptions."

Kroner smiled. "It is not the magazine of which I speak. I speak of books in which life is probed and analyzed. I speak of the eternal struggle between man and woman to communicate."

"You mean dirty books," I said.

"Never dirty." Kroner was angry. "Books of the

soul. Books of man's innermost desires. Books that everyone bought. Everyone. I was so rich. And then the politicians decide they will decide what the public should read."

"Did they ban the books?" Trudy asked.

"Of course not. I would have no problems if they did. No, they changed the law and allowed all books to be published. There was to be no censorship of any kind. My publishing house crumbled. With so many life books for sale, the people turned to other kinds of books; books that did not speak of man and woman. Trash. Novels. Spy books. History and biographies and Gothic novels and nurse books and animal books. The government has been the ruination of Denmark . . . and of Vognen Kroner."

"We're sorry, Mr. Kroner," I said. He seemed very upset.

"You should be. No, I don't mean that. It is not your fault. In America, your government was sensible. It banned life books and that caused Americans to want to buy them. But even America is now allowing too many books and movies to reach the public. Even in America people are becoming tired and bored with sex in books and films. At one time, we could depend upon selling much of our work in America. Now, your country can no longer be depended upon. This is why I am forced to begin a new career as a film producer. My hopes ride high with Ollie Borehol."

"Is he a good filmmaker?" Trudy asked.

"*Ja*. But he is also bright and imaginative in planning to make his films popular in America."

"How is he going to do that, Mr. Kroner?"

"Ollie realizes that there are certain institutions in America that are sacred. Such as football, astronauts and the Supreme Court. We will produce a series of life films in which football players and astronauts and judges are involved in healthy perversion. This will

cause the films to be banned in America and we will
make a fortune. Do you understand?"

"Yes."

They were ready to film. Ollie took us aside and
instructed us to enter through the apartment door,
look around, see Stud and smile a warm welcome. We
did what he wanted.

"Good, good," Ollie exclaimed. "Excellent. Now,
I change the camera angle and we do the next scene."
Ollie talked to us again and told us we were to go
to Stud Swensen and embrace him.

"Do we have to do that?" I asked. One of the
Danish girls snickered. I glared at her and my dream
came back to me. I'd show them. I'd give Stud an
embrace like he never had before from any Danish
blonde. The camera rolled and Trudy and I approached Stud. I wrapped my arms around his neck
and gave him a kiss. Trudy tried to sneak in between
us and managed to kiss his arm. The camera continued to roll, tilting down a little as Stud slipped his
hand down and started making circles on my fanny. I
pulled back and told him to watch that stuff. Two
of the Danish girls snickered this time and Ollie was
very upset.

"Why did you pull away?" he screamed at me.

"Because he put his hand down there."

"Of course he put his hand down there. He loves
you."

"We've never met before," I snarled.

"That is right. It is instant love between you. It is
the force of the man and the woman."

"Well, I don't like it," I said.

"Me, too," Trudy added.

Ollie babbled to Mr. Kroner and told us to do the
scene over again. We did, and Stud kept his hands
above the hips.

"Good," Ollie exclaimed. "Now, in the next scene,

we bring you together in the ultimate form of man and woman together. Take off your clothes." Stud immediately dropped his loin cloth and grinned at us. I tried to appear disinterested and started up a ridiculous conversation with Trudy about what color drapes we'd get for our apartment in New York. I was pushing avocado when Ollie confronted us.

"Come on now, Trudy and Rachel. Take off your clothes. It is time for the love scene."

"Don't be ridiculous," I said, laughing nervously.

Ollie threw another fit. He pleaded with Mr. Kroner to intervene. He pleaded with Inga to talk to us and convince us there was nothing wrong with nudity in films. This whole time, Stud Swensen stood talking to the blondes. They giggled and talked about the same things we'd stand and talk about with fellows in Bloomingdale's, only everybody keeps their clothing on in Bloomingdale's. Stud Swensen would cause quite a scene back on Third Avenue.

Kroner checked his watch. "We are losing time, Ollie. And time is money, my money. You have already established the film with the two American stewardesses. They have already embraced Stud. So use other girls for the love scenes. Do not show their faces. Who will know?"

"I cannot do that," Ollie protested. "How can one film love without showing faces?"

"Nonsense, Ollie. I learned long ago that the people do not care about the faces. Faces they can see all day on the street. Forget the faces."

Ollie agreed reluctantly. He snapped his fingers and the four blonde beauties slipped out of their clothes. "No, no, no," Ollie said. "I need only two." Ollie chose his pair and the remaining girls sat on the floor and pouted.

"Well, I guess we'll leave," Trudy said as lightly as she could. It was the wrong thing to say. Ollie and

Kroner stepped between us and the door and told us we'd have to remain during the entire shooting.

"You see," Ollie explained, "we need your American voices. If this film were to be shown in Denmark, we would not need you. But nobody goes to see these life films in Denmark any more. We must turn to America for the market. But in your country, there must be what is called redeeming social value to each movie. To give this film such social value, we will use your voices at certain times. Besides, we have already photographed the establishing scenes in which the audience knows the film is about two American airline stewardesses. Even the title of the film is being photographed at the graphics studio."

"What is the title, Ollie?"

"I Am Curious: Red White and Blue."

"Lovely."

"Ja. You stay. OK?"

"OK."

We spent the next six hours alternating between shock, amazement, boredom, interest, and stifled laughter. Stud Swensen and his two partners (our stunt men, you might say) went through all the positions in the marriage manuals plus a few creative variations on the basic drill. We were called upon to speak three times. The first instance was after position number two had been completed. On cue, which was a loud moan of release from Stud, I said, "The flight was long. The air congestion is bad and must be solved." The audience would think one of the girls in the pile on the mattress had said this and, because it touched on a real problem faced by many citizens, would help the film achieve redeeming social value in the U. S. Courts.

Trudy performed the second time. She said, "Tomorrow we fly to Vietnam. Tonight we love." She did it with a lot of feeling, and Ollie seemed pleased.

Finally, I was called upon to say, "My trip to Denmark has been good for me. I know now of love." I gave it my all and everyone beamed.

We all went to dinner after the shooting and had a marvelous time. We'd grown fond of the crew and stars of the love scene, and by the time we were to check in for our return flight, I'd completely gotten over my dread of Denmark and all those blonde beauties. In fact, I'd come to realize just how foolish my fears had been. I mentioned it to Trudy on the flight home.

"You know, Trudy, I was really a dope worrying about competing with the blonde Danish girls. Did you notice they aren't real blondes at all?"

"Yup, I sure did. Boy, what lengths they'll go to to perpetuate a myth, huh, Rach?"

EPILOGUE: We got to see a very rough, edited version of the film during our last trip to Copenhagen that month. Ollie had done a superb job of working scenes around so that the audience would think it was Trudy and me on the mattress with Stud Swensen. You'd think the audience would find it strange that the girl's faces were never shown during the love scenes, but Mr. Kroner was probably right. You don't look for faces when you go to see a film rated "X"—Restricted to those 50 years of age and over.

Fortunately for us, the film was never released in America. In fact, the only places Ollie could find to distribute the film were Guatemala and Chile, and since none of our relatives live in those countries, our reputations are still intact.

We've seen Inga a few times since our Copenhagen experience, and she informs us that Ollie is now working for the Danish Post Office. Mr. Kroner is in business selling underground imitations of Georg Jensen silver to tourists. All in all, everyone involved seems to have found themselves.

"Skål!"

CHAPTER VI

"Back To The Wall"

We made sure, as Karl had warned us, to take the U-Bahn and not the S-Bahn train. The S-train keeps going past East Berlin into Soviet-controlled East Germany. We didn't want to go *that* far. We only wanted to spend a day on the other side of the wall. Actually we had no stomach for making the trip at all. It's just that our Captain had been born and raised in Germany. And Germans never give up. Although he had been an American citizen for years, he was constantly rooting for West Germany the way some people do for their favorite football team. West Berlin was alma mater to him. He wanted everyone to experience the pride he felt over the way West Germany had restored itself to the third or fourth richest nation in the world while Soviet-controlled East Germany kept slipping behind. So we promised to make the trip to keep things happy between us. He was like a Father Hen giving us instructions and directions.

We knew enough to wear inconspicuous clothes. You've got to be careful to look dowdy. A Paris scarf or a pair of yellow plastic boots is enough to stop traffic and you might as well wear a sign. So we fished out our drabbest outfits, tucked our precious passports in our pockets, left most of our dollars and West German marks in the hotel, and headed for the subway.

Our Captain also gave us the address of a distant cousin of his who lived in the Eastern Zone of Berlin. He wanted us to stop in and visit her. "I'm sure she'll be glad to see you."

"Won't she get into trouble if they find her entertaining Western visitors?" Trudy wondered.

"No," the Captain assured us. "I talked to her on my last trip and she said it would be OK."

It was more risky for onetime German citizens to visit East Berlin than for Americans. U.S. passports still show your place of birth. Sometimes a German dateline under place of birth was enough to get one detained as a possible espionage agent. We wondered why the Captain would take the risk and bother just to be kind to so distant a cousin.

"I didn't see her," he said. "I just telephoned her."

We hear so much about the wall dividing the East and West we forget that the radio and television and even the telephone makes a joke of cement walls, Iron Curtains and barbed wire.

So we promised, and now we had to visit his relatives to keep everybody happy.

So much of West Berlin was destroyed and then rebuilt it is certainly one of the newest looking and most modern cities in Europe. On top of that, American and international pop art gives it a Western flavor. The words on the billboards and outdoor advertising and neon signs may be in German, but the symbols are international. It's the first thing you miss after you've reached East Berlin.

All the streets look grey without the neon lights; the windows seem bare and grim. Drugstores are no longer recognizable as drug stores. The automobile traffic thins out and there seem to be more people walking.

By noon, we had had enough. We were ready to head back.

"How about the Captain's cousin, Rachel?"

"Let's not and say we did," I suggested. "I don't exactly feel like knocking on doors in this town."

"What are we going to say when he asks us?" The thought of being interrogated by our brisk, efficient Teutonic Captain was more forbidding than the Communist policeman we saw on the corner. We asked directions. Our German was good enough for that. But to understand what the policeman said, even with gestures, seemed hopeless. That's the trouble with all the phrase books ever sold. The wrong people buy them. Unless the people giving directions have the same book as you do, you're lost. But the policeman was very nice. He hailed a youngster and practically ordered him to escort us to a tiny grey townhouse on a pretty side street. The neighborhood was in much better shape than some parts of the city we had hiked through. The front door was freshly painted in soft grey and there were red and yellow flowers lining the walk. On the second floor, window boxes bloomed with the same flowers. We flipped a coin and Trudy lost, so she climbed the steps and knocked at the door. I stayed on the sidewalk, trying to figure how to get back to the subway station in a hurry. I thought I spotted a man's face at the window, peering at me from behind a lace curtain.

"OK, Trudy, we tried," I shouted. "We can tell the Captain we tried. There's nobody home." I was all for getting back to the other side. Trudy stood there bravely. When she finally turned and started down the stairs, the door opened a crack. Then a smiling middle-aged woman swung it open wide.

"Ja?" she asked. All Trudy's Berlitz German went down the drain. She copped out.

"Do you speak English?" I asked.

"Ja," the woman said. I had the note from the Captain in my purse so I rushed up the stairs and handed it to her.

"You must be girls from the airlines. You are so pretty," she said, taking the note I handed her. "Ah, Karl sent you.

"He was always a very determined boy. Likes to get his own way," she said. She asked us oodles of questions about flying. Where we had been, what cities we had liked best, how things looked to us in West Berlin. When I mentioned the Wall our hostess smiled and said nothing. Clearly, this was a political question and her answer was a determined *No Comment*. We had vowed we were not going to bring up anything political, but the Wall dominated your thoughts.

"Ah, yes, ze Wall," our hostess mumbled after a minute. "We have a guest here, just the person you should speak to concerning our Wall. He is working for many years, writing a book about it."

"Oh, how interesting," Trudy said. Nobody would ever suspect we were literary types from the West. But with one book under our belt, we discovered we were like brand new mothers on the subject of children. We were experts. Whenever someone said the word book, a certain light went on in our eyes.

"Does he speak English?" I asked as an afterthought. I didn't feel up to a three-cornered conversation with our hostess doubling as an interpreter. That can be exhausting. It takes a half hour for a simple sentence to make the rounds.

"Oh, yes, indeed," said our hostess. "He is a Professor at our University." With that, she beckoned to the Professor and we joined the party. The drink we had been offered tasted very strange but interesting. Some kind of punch was my guess. I finished mine in a hurry and they offered me another. With a sly warning. It was spiked with kirschwasser which I gathered was fruity and sneaky. I promised to be careful. Anyway, neither of us was driving. All we had to do was make the S-Bahn.

The hostess introduced us to the professor as Airline Stewardesses from America. The Professor puffed on a dead pipe, then tried to stuff it and re-light it. When I offered him an American cigarette he dropped the warm pipe in his pocket and eagerly accepted.

"What kind of book are you writing on the Wall, Professor?" I asked him.

"Well, I think perhaps you might characterize it as a psychological study," he began. "I take case histories of those persons who have *defected* to the West. I am attempting to find certain things in common in their disturbed mental states."

"Oh," Trudy said. He seemed to be saying that anyone who tried to escape from East Germany was clearly off their rocker—a mental case. I don't know why I was surprised. If he was a Professor at the University he'd have to be a member of the Communist Party, or close to it. And if you wanted to get a book published in East Germany, you'd have to be some kind of a cheerleader for *their* side. I felt the conversation was getting too political and I didn't want to pursue it. He couldn't sway me and I knew I couldn't budge him. But Trudy was in there pitching.

"You don't have to be insane to prefer freedom, do you?" she asked. I could feel ice forming all over the room. There was a great yawning silence.

"My friend and I enjoyed your punch very much," I said to our hostess. "Did you tell her about the kirschwasser? Trudy," I said, "that punch is loaded. Let's keep the conversation light. You know."

But Trudy held her ground. Finally the Professor smiled, nodded his head, ducked the question and started all over again.

"We understand, of course, that America makes very much of a word called Freedom. But what does it amount to? I am free to work and to study and to meet with my friends, to eat my meals, to smoke my pipe, and to sleep. The people of East Berlin are free of traffic congestion. They are free from . . . smog, I believe you call it. We are free of the pressures of a capitalist society which encourages us to work every moment in order to buy a larger automobile, a larger

house, a larger bank account. Freedom is largely a
state of mind, don't you think so, ladies? And the
state of mind is largely based on the biochemistry of
the body. A prisoner feels free if he is given the right
kind of drugs, is it not so?"

"You may have a point there, Professor," I conceded.

"I can't see it," Trudy insisted. I thought we ought
to be heading back to the hotel. I was afraid the
kirschwasser was changing Trudy's chemistry. I felt
it was the wrong place and the wrong time to wave
the flag.

"It's early, Rachel," she kept saying. "Besides I'm
enjoying the Professor's conversation. This is the first
East-West dialogue I've ever had."

"There you are," said the Professor. "When we are
talking together, we both feel free. The world is too
small any more for shouting at one another."

Karl's cousin invited us for dinner. I thought that
was a bit much. I was determined to cross back to
West Berlin before dark.

"Never mind," said our hostess. "We'll eat early
and you will have plenty of time."

We had another glass of punch and more conversation. But no matter where the discussion began, it always dead-ended at the Wall. It seemed to dominate
our little dinner party as it dominates the lives of most
Berliners. The Professor made it easy for us to talk
with him. He never tried to press his philosophy on
us. He was content to listen to anything we had to say.
He was detached, philosophical, but a staunch Marxist
of the old school. There was no budging him and no
point, really, in trying.

Dinner was like Luchow's without the music. Erben-
suppe, a delicious sort of pea soup; Rinderwurst, a
beef frankfurter, and the inevitable dumplings. East
German dumplings are not exactly light and fluffy like

Betty Crocker's, but they were the perfect antidote to the kirschwasser. By the time we got to the coffee and strudel we were sober as judges.

"The interesting thing," the Professor was saying, "is this state of mind called freedom. If a man thinks he does not have it, he will do anything to pursue it. Rightly or wrongly, he will act, is it not so?"

"Yes," said Trudy. "Exactly."

"But why? What will cause a man to crash his automobile through barbed wire and concrete? Freedom is not a *place*. What will compel a man to dig a tunnel for weeks, even months in search of this thing called freedom? What will send a man running like an animal across open fields strung with barbed wire, in clear view of guards with long-range weapons?"

"Someone once said 'Give me liberty or give me death,'" Trudy declaimed.

"Yes, but not all of them die. Some find their way to West Berlin and find themselves not so free. Here they were relatively free. There they are relatively less free, unless they have plenty of money. It is all quite absurd to me. But of course, unless it happens, there is no book for me to write. Is there?"

"Have you been to West Berlin, Professor," I asked.

"Yes. Yes. Once Berlin was one. When the city was divided I chose to remain here. Until recently I traveled freely to the West, lecturing and studying. I was allowed because my position was beyond question. Unfortunately, another Professor from the University acted foolishly and stayed in West Berlin during one of his trips. Since then, I have not traveled so frequently. But it does not matter. I lecture as well here as there. My friends come here or I go to them. What does it matter?"

Suddenly it was dark outside. Pitch black.

"Oh, my," our hostess said. "You must leave before it is too late. Are you sure you can find the train?"

"I have it all worked out in my head," I explained. But she started confusing me with more directions.

"These young American ladies deserve a German-speaking escort," the Professor said. "I can drive you to the crossing point."

"All the way to Checkpoint Charlie?"

"They will allow you to cross there," the Professor said. It seemed a strange way for the evening to end. But after all, politics or no politics, the Professor seemed like a true gentleman of the old school. And also, like Karl, something of a German Father Hen, as far as young girls were concerned. After all, if two German girls came to Louisville, I'm sure my father would insist on driving them to the bus station.

We thanked our hostess, and the Professor hurried us to his little green sedan. The streets seemed virtually deserted. Traffic slowed down to the merest trickle as we got closer to Checkpoint Charlie. The Professor was still expounding on the psychological quirks of people who tried to escape to the West.

"It probably has something to do with the masculine ego. The male ego feeds on such a challenge. If a man is not sure of his masculinity he needs to perform some feat like climbing the Matterhorn or breaching the Wall. The Wall becomes a symbol of challenge."

"Like the moon," I suggested.

"Not quite," the Professor said. "The Russian Cosmonauts, even your Astronauts, are quite different symbols. Symbols of the superiority of collective effort. There is really little rivalry there between our two systems."

We didn't argue.

"I follow escape attempts closely," the Professor said as he slowed down to light his pipe, holding it out the window to fan the embers. "And yet I rarely hear of an escape in which men take advantage of man's greatest weaknesses."

"What are they, Professor?" Trudy wanted to know.

"Why, money, of course," he said, "and pretty girls."

"Of course," I said.

"It is difficult for a man here to accumulate enough money to make it interesting as a bribe for our guards at the border. But we do have our pretty girls."

I remembered reading about an American girl who served three years in an East German prison for helping some East German to escape. But I had no idea what she had done, and how they caught her. "How could a pretty girl help a man to escape to West Berlin?" Trudy asked.

"It would be simple, I imagine," the Professor smiled. "A pretty girl goes to a certain point on the Wall and engages them in conversation. She is dressed a certain way. Perhaps she flirts a little. Depending on the situation, the guards might be lonely and expect to take advantage of the opportunity, despite their orders against being distracted."

"That's been done too many times in the movies," Trudy said.

"Perhaps you are right. A girl knows more about these things than an old Professor."

"Quit calling yourself old, Professor," I said. "We think you're very attractive and very sweet."

"Yes," said Trudy. "I always did like men who smoke pipes."

We were approaching the neutral zone between the Russian and the American sectors of the city and the Professor slowed down. He parked his little green sedan behind some trees which shielded us from the sight of the two Russian guards who patrolled one section of the neutral area. The floodlights lighted the no-man's land between the two borders. It was one of the great tourist sights in Europe, more exciting for the life and death danger that seemed to lurk in every shadow. Not as beautiful as the Vatican or the Champs Elysées, but still so eerie it gave you goosebumps to be so close to it after having seen it recreated in the movies so many times.

There was no traffic; we could hear the sound of the soldiers' boots as they marched across the floodlit pavement.

"Take a look at them," the Professor said. "They're just young men. Boys from Kief or Pilsen. With sweethearts far away somewhere. A pretty girl could interest them for at least five minutes. A man could race across the neutral zone in half that time."

"Then why hasn't anyone done it?" Trudy wanted to know.

"For two reasons," the Professor said calmly. "First, few men would want to owe their life or escape to the sacrifice of some woman. Second, few women would be willing to risk their lives in that way. If they loved a man that much, they would not want to let him get away."

I could understand that. We watched the guards making their continued rounds, their bodies silhouetted against the floodlights of the city. I imagined Richard Burton running and Liz Taylor playing hanky panky with the guards. Or Clint Eastwood running and Tuesday Weld batting her eyelashes at the stern young Russian soldiers.

"What would they do to a girl who was caught?"

"It would depend on who she is. If she was a girl from East Germany they would immediately suspect collaboration. But for girls like you, for instance, there would be no danger. It would depend on how clever the man was. If he made his dash without being seen, the guards would never know at all."

"I guess not," Trudy said. "But the whole idea gives me the shivers."

"It's hardly worth it, is it? It is one thing to say 'Give me liberty or give me death.' It is another thing to mean it."

I was glad it was Trudy who had quoted Patrick Henry and not me. It was a real dig and she asked for it.

"Well, Professor," I said, "You've been very sweet and terribly interesting, but we had better get going."

"I understand," he said. "It is late. But wait. I have an idea. It would be amusing, would it not, to put my premise to a test. You seem skeptical that two armed soldiers could be distracted by a pretty face. I suspect otherwise. But two pretty faces. Let's see who is right. You walk to the guards, tell them you are girls from an American airline. You have lost your way. Ask them directions. Show them your passports. Try and communicate with them. I will sit here and keep time with my watch. See how long you can distract them. It will make an amusing incident for my book. The crossing is only a few thousand yards beyond."

I wanted to confide to him that it would make an interesting little tidbit for our book, too, providing the East German prisons didn't frown on creative writing.

For some strange reason Trudy was game. It would take something even stranger to change her into the cautious type. We didn't agree to anything. We knew enough about conspiracy indictments to know that even intending to do something can count against you. We didn't say a word except "thank you" and "good night." We didn't say we would and we didn't say we wouldn't. Like true international adventuresses, we kept our mystery. We got out of the car and walked from the trees toward the floodlight area. We were within spitting distance of the guards before one of them raised his rifle, pointed it directly at us and hollered "Halt!" We stopped in our tracks and started babbling in English. Cautiously, they moved toward us. Then they stopped and said something which sounded like "Coming zee here." When someone hollers in German it sounds very much like English. We knew he wanted us to advance so we walked to him.

I pulled my green passport out of my pocket and started waving it.

"Maedchen in Uniform. Lufthansa," Trudy kept saying, while she spread her arms like a Boeing 747. "S-Bahn. Hotel," she cried pitifully. She was lost because she couldn't remember the word for lost. We were in over our head. We were lost. We looked lost and sounded lost. We gave a performance that couldn't have been rehearsed. They were suspicious at first. They looked us up and down.

One soldier tried to take my passport but I wouldn't let go. We were eyeball to eyeball now and I was really frightened. They chattered to one another and then said "Americanische?"

It was a very welcome question. One we could answer in perfect German. We must have said "Ja, ja" a hundred times. Now they looked us over more like boys and less like soldiers. They must have been interested in the way we looked because one soldier broke into a lovely smile. Then they lowered their rifles and began to laugh at us. We began laughing ourselves.

"Berlin Hilton Hotel," I said, pointing in a direction I thought was West. I got back a long answer I didn't understand. Finally, the second soldier began speaking a halting English, with a British accent.

"You should not be alone here like zis," he lectured us.

"We lost our way," Trudy said.

"What part of America are you from?" he asked us.

"I'm from Kentucky," I said. "Trudy is from Texas. But we live in New York now."

"Is zis your first time in Berlin?"

"Yes."

"You like Berlin?"

"We haven't seen very much of it," Trudy said.

"We love what we've seen," I felt compelled to add diplomatically.

They began chattering with one another in German and then the younger one made us an offer in English.

"We are off duty at eight o'clock. Perhaps you could meet wiz us at ze cafe for two hours."

That's the military for you, making a date on-the-hour-by-the-hour. We both smiled and fluttered but allowed as we had a date on the other side and were frantic because we were so late.

"Maybe we could come back another night," Trudy suggested, shifting her weight from one foot to the other. That seemed to turn the trick. They smiled at one another the way men do when they think they have made an impression.

I struggled to say "Auf Wiedersehn" because I thought it meant "See you later, Alligator," or " 'Til we meet again." They clicked their heels, bowed politely and directed us toward Checkpoint Charlie.

Those few thousand yards seemed like miles as we walked with our backs to East Berlin. Every few hundred feet Trudy turned and waved to make sure they didn't have their guns trained on us. Breathing heavily, we crossed into West Berlin. We hailed a cab and drove silently to the hotel.

It wasn't until we were in our room we both realized we had an acute need to go to the bathroom.

"How long do you think we spent talking to the guards, Rachel?" Trudy asked.

"It seemed like forever. Five minutes at least."

"Do you think the Professor tried to make a run for it?"

I had to admit it had crossed my mind. If I had heard a volley of shots while we were crossing no-man's-land I wouldn't really have been surprised.

"Nonsense, Trudy," I said. "He's a hard-core Communist if I ever met one."

"Well, how many hard-core Communists have you ever talked to? In spy movies people are never what they seem to be. If someone *seems* to be a hard-core Communist, that's when you have to watch it."

"Sure, but it was all so *accidental*. We didn't have any idea we were going to visit Karl's cousin. So how could he?"

"Semper Paratus," Trudy said. "If you were looking to escape, you'd always be prepared. You'd lay awake nights thinking of a hundred ways. You'd be ready to take advantage of any situation."

"You think the Professor really . . . took advantage of us?"

"Why not? Isn't it possible?"

I immediately bolted the hotel door and drew the blinds. Then I began to get the shivers and the shakes. I got into bed and covered myself with one of those marvelous fluffy goosefeather quilts the German hotel maids lay out for you.

We had to check in at Templehof Airdrome in Berlin the next morning for our flight back to Rome. So we got up early and took a taxi back to the Wall. We felt like criminals returning to the scene of the caper. It looks different by day and it's hard to get one's bearings. We were about to leave when Trudy pointed across the neutral zone to the little patch of woods where the Professor had parked last night.

"Look, Rach."

"Yeah," I said. "I guess that's the patch of trees."

"But look at the car. The green sedan. It's a car just like the Professor's. It's still parked there by the trees."

She was right. It *was* the Professor's car. Or another green sedan exactly like it.

"Do you think he got across while we were with the guards?"

"I don't know," I said.

"Maybe he couldn't get the car started and he walked home."

"Yeah, maybe," I said. "That's probably exactly what happened."

"Will the Real Spy
Please Stand Up"

I never expected to flip over the first Russian I laid eyes on. But this Cossack was too gorgeous to be ignored. We couldn't ignore him even if we were demented enough to *want* to. There he sat in all his Eurasian glory, perched on a high stool in a little compartment where the foreign passenger traffic trickles through single file.

"Dig *that*," I said to Trudy. He was tall, with a grey Astrakhan fur hat on top of his smooth dark hair at just the right rakish angle. His grey Cossack blouse was tight as a new body shirt, rippling over stupendous muscles. His broad shoulders were accented by little epaulets with tiny red pips on them. His wide leather belt helped him to show off his waistline and he wore soft leather boots. "Do you suppose we can get lucky enough to get searched?" I wondered.

The Moscow Airport Terminal is a huge barn of a place, and it seemed to be completely empty except for our incoming flight. Everybody seemed to be coming in and nobody seemed to be leaving. One of the two groups of college students on our trip was being sorted out by their teacher-escorts, with some help from a lady guide from Intourist. There was a complication. The Russian visas for a half-dozen students had not come through. They had left without them and now they were going to have to stay overnight at the airport until the Red red tape could be untangled. If the handsome Red Commissar was going to spend the night with them, I was going to be jealous.

I was afraid the confusion and delay might induce some supervisor to put on another passport inspector. I didn't want to be hustled through a different checkout counter. I wanted to wait until the very last so I could get his undivided attention.

"If you're cold, sweetie, you go on ahead," I said to Trudy.

"After you," she said, smiling sweetly.

"I thought you hated cops and Communists," I said.

"He's not a cop, he's a Russian GI," she said. "Besides, it's Christmas time and we're supposed to love everybody." That's why we took the Russian run, on account of the holidays. We had had it up to here with the whole phoney pushy status-happy Christmas gift-giving thing and, one day when Trudy said she'd like to spend the holidays where they never *heard* of Christmas, I suggested bidding for the Moscow run. It was a joke at first. But it turned out most stews were not wild about the Moscow run, which left the field wide open. We had our little joke and now we were stuck with it. It had been a long trip and a tiring one, but things were looking up. With two whole days and nights in Moscow to look forward to, we were ready to adjourn the cold war for a bit and have a ball. Our captain, first officer and flight engineer had made the Moscow run before, and gave us orientation lectures and briefings on what to do and what not to do. But nobody said anything helpful about Russian men. Another stew of our acquaintance claimed to be completely turned off by Russian males. She sneered at them for wearing old-fashioned floppy wide bottom trousers, and claimed they all had enormous behinds. Well, bell bottom trousers had come back with a bang. Cossack shirts and furs were the latest male fashions. Big behinds might be the next rage.

"Did you get a look at his rear end?" Trudy asked.

"No," I admitted. "I think some people have been

giving us bum steers. Trying to discourage competition," I added, checking over my make-up.

"Besides, how could they dance the way they do without getting muscles?"

"Exactly," I said, as we approached our turn.

At the last moment a male passenger from Brooklyn appeared. Gallantly, he invited us to go ahead of him. We out-maneuvered him in a hurry, insisting that regulations required all passengers be cleared ahead of the crew.

"Is this your first time in Moscow?" he asked.

"Why, yes," we admitted.

"Oh, you have a great experience ahead of you," he beamed. "If there's anything I can help you with, I'd be more than happy to oblige."

"Thanks very much," I smiled.

"I'm staying at the Hotel Metropol," he added.

"We're staying at the Metropol, too," I shouted, hoping the handsome Cossack could hear me over the chatter.

"I've been a member of the Communist Party for years," he whispered, confidentially.

Now he tells us, I thought. That and five kopecks will probably get him on the Moscow subway. The gorgeous Commissar looked at his passport photo, looked at his face, then looked inside his passport for his three-part visa. He banged it with a stamp, tore off one part of the visa and sent the Brooklyn Red on his way.

Our big moment was at hand. The Cossack was even better-looking at close range. He had nice olive skin and eye lashes long enough to make any girl jealous. He looked at my passport and then looked at me. I smiled.

"This is my first time on the Moscow run," I said, dropping my glove.

"Welcome to the Soviet Union," he said in perfect English.

"We're only going to be here for two days," Trudy said, dropping her purse.

"You are traveling together?" he asked with just a hint of a smile.

"Yes, but we're not married," I said. I don't know why I was in such a hurry to get that in. Now he looked Trudy over as she handed him her passport.

"We hope you have a very pleasant stay in our country," he said. He wasn't exactly cold. But I knew we weren't getting through to him. We picked our scattered accessories up off the radiant heated floor. Meanwhile, I tried to think of something suspicious I could say or do which might prolong the encounter. Usually border guards and customs functionaries are so boring and unattractive you just want to get it over with, without giving them a second look. I would have shouted "Down with Stalin!" but everybody in the USSR was down on Stalin anyway, so that would get us nowhere. "Down with Khrushchev!" was old hat, too. I was ready to make a rude remark about any official in the Kremlin, but I couldn't think of one name. Desperate to do something that would bring me under suspicion, I took a crazy chance.

"Have you got the pot, Trudy?" I said, "or did we leave it in our duffle bag?"

"Have I got *what?*" she said. She can be so dense when she's not absolutely brilliant.

"The pot!" I said, practically shouting. "I feel like turning on. I can't last. It may take hours to get to the Metropol Hotel."

"Oh," said Trudy, finally catching on. "I thought *you* had it."

"Where?"

"In the money belt under your girdle," she said.

You bitchy thing, you, I thought, as I began examining my perfect size 12 figure for imaginary contraband lumps. Praise Allah, at last we were getting a rise out of him. He raised himself to his full height of twelve feet, six inches, and began shouting in a loud voice. His throaty Russian syllables were like music. *Now* we were getting somewhere. A young lady in her twenties, with no make-up, long black hair and a chic Red stocking hat came running in answer to his shouted commands.

"Perhaps I can help you," she said to Trudy, smiling. "Come this way."

"Oh, no," I thought. "Don't tell me they're such big Puritans they insist on having *women* search you for contraband. That's not *fair*." But it was too late. We had our story and we were stuck with it.

She escorted us down a long marble corridor. Then she stopped in front of the door and said, "Here you are, please." We walked in. But the Russian lady didn't even bother to follow. We knew why when we heard the first sound of a Soviet Socialist waterfall. We were in the ladies room.

The rest of the crew was waiting for us by the limousine. Larry Frye, our flight engineer, had looked all over for us.

"I thought maybe you got into trouble," he said when he found us.

"We tried, but didn't make it," I lamented.

We tried every way to get another glimmer of our handsome Commissar, but his little booth was empty. After him, every Russian male we saw, uniformed or not, was an anti-climax. They sure know what they're doing, the Russians, putting their best foot forward. The U. S. could do worse than draft some good-looking men like Steve McQueen or Paul Newman to check in foreign tourists at New York International Airport. Of course, they couldn't wear Astrakhan hats and Cossack blouses. But they could come up with something that was American, like cowboy outfits with lots of leather fringe.

We had to fill out huge forms listing every item of

gold we were carrying on our person or in our luggage. "Put everything down, and then some," Larry warned us.

"What's this for?" I wanted to know.

"It's illegal to take gold out of Russia. You can get thirty years for trying to smuggle out one little earring."

"Then we'll be thoroughly searched on the way out?"

"You better believe it."

"Oh, that's marvelous," I said.

"What good will that do?" Trudy mumbled. "Handsome will probably be off-duty."

Larry thought we weren't serious enough about the possible perils and he kept warning us to be careful about our conversation. "Don't talk too much in the limousine. We have a Russian driver. If you want to talk over something important, remember your hotel room is probably bugged."

"So what if it is?" I said.

"So don't get me in trouble. If you have any wild ideas, call me and we'll meet downstairs in the street to talk."

"Larry, you're putting us on," Trudy said.

"Better safe than sorry, kiddo," he insisted. Everybody was so silent on the drive into Moscow I couldn't stand it. As we got closer to the inner city, I thought I saw a man dragging a Christmas tree down the street. When I saw another one, I knew I hadn't been hallucinating. Then I saw a Christmas tree hanging by a rope outside an apartment window. I kept my mouth shut about it until we got to Gorki Street. It looked like Fifth Avenue in December. The street signs and lampposts were decked with colored lights in red and white and green. I saw a huge figure in one of the store windows. If that wasn't Santa Claus, I wasn't in Moscow.

"Look, Trudy," I said. "Maybe somebody put LSD in my coffee. Is this town all decorated for Christmas or isn't it?"

"I just saw Santa Claus in a window," Trudy said.

"Thank you, Miss Baker," I said.

When we got within sight of the Kremlin, we saw a huge Christmas tree in the square. It had millions of lights on it and a big red star on the top. The entire center of the city was decorated with lights and festive trimmings, with snow flakes and red candles and all the other holdiday trimmings, including Father Christmas himself.

"Where did we get the idea you could escape Christmas by coming to Russia?" we wanted to know.

"They don't celebrate Christmas, they celebrate the New Year," Larry Frye insisted. "Everybody does, even the Chinese. They just put the decorations up early."

"Have you been here for the holidays before?" we asked him. Of course he hadn't. He was guessing just like we were. Here was something we had to get to the bottom of.

U. S. airline crews always stay at the Hotel Metropol, a big, hollow hangar-type place where President Nixon stayed when he was in Moscow. The doorman and porter take charge of your luggage and once they've installed you, you never see another male member of the staff. There aren't any. The corridors in the Metropol are as wide as some streets in Paris. And at the top of the stairs on every floor, a woman of certain age sits there, the keeper of the keys and Lord knows what else.

"They have Big Mommas on every floor?" I wondered. "This is worse than stew school," I said to Larry Frye.

"It's the concierge system," he said. "Just like in Paris."

"In Paris they encourage the sort of thing I'm thinking of. These women look very discouraging," I said.

"They work 24 hours a day," Larry explained.

They did look tired and discouraged, at least the lady on our floor.

The first morning, Trudy and I decided to brave the cold and snow. We bundled up to the eyes, wrapped ourselves in fur coats and wore our tallest boots. We wanted to disappear into the masses of people, listen to them, see them close up. We knew everyone was going to ask us if the people looked happy or seemed to be sad. You can't tell unless you get close.

We didn't know which way to turn, right or left. But we had to start somewhere. Cars seemed to be moving in the streets but the snow made everything so quiet. No congestion, no honking horns, no cursing taxi drivers, no people talking with their hands like in Rome, or with their faces like in Paris. Hardly any talking at all. It was eerie.

We reached the corner when a man passed by and brushed my arm. He stopped, looked around, and spoke to us in English with a Russian accent.

"Hey, pooseykat," he said. "I give you three for one."

We ignored him and walked straight ahead until we got to the huge crossing. We looked back and saw him watching us. We turned and started back towards the hotel. Now he was walking beside us. He was tall and dark, with a heavy coat, a dark caracul hat with ear muffs, a heavy scarf and tinted Peter Fonda goggles. He had a grin that was watermelon wide. One gold tooth gleamed through clouds of his steamy breath as the almost horizontal sun caught it and picked up light. With the goggles and muffler, you're suddenly seeing people the way a dentist sees them. All the rest is covered. We kept moving and he kept grinning.

"American student. Welcome to Moscow," he said.

"Do you think he's really an American student?" Trudy whispered to me.

"No, silly. He thinks we're American students," I said.

"That's sort of nice," she said, smiling at him.

"I shook hands with Richard Nixon in Moscow when he was here," he said. "Pepsi Cola very good. I know many Americans. You can trust me. I give you three for one."

Why were we being so unfriendly, I wondered. Nobody was following us yet. We were just meeting a man in the street. This is why we had gone out walking in the first place.

"Thank you very much," I said, smiling graciously. I was just about to ask him what he wanted to give us three *what* for one *what*—and he was gone.

People kept passing us, masses of them. But nobody his size with one gold tooth and wearing Peter Fonda goggles.

"I don't know why we were so unfriendly," I said to Trudy. "Larry told us to be careful what we said in the hotel room because that was bugged. But he said it's safe to talk in the street. And nobody is following us yet."

"Maybe not us," said Trudy, "but maybe they're following *him*."

Anyway, he was gone, disappeared without a trace. "What was he talking about giving us three for one?"

"I have no idea," I said. "Remember to put it in our diary. Make a note and we'll ask Larry."

We didn't dare stop walking or we would freeze to death. We went under the boulevard into a heated pedestrian passageway. On the newsstand there were boring-looking magazines that all looked secondhand. A man was selling lemons out of a basket. People were stopping and buying one lemon at a time. Two at the most.

I figured we had to start shopping somewhere. So I smiled at him and handed him a ruble and held up my one finger. He gave me one lemon and fifty kopecks change. That was my first lesson in Russian arithmetic. A lemon in winter costs fifty kopecks, or the price of ten subway fares.

After we came out of the passageway we saw two women selling something else in the street. We didn't know what it was, but there were two lines of customers waiting in the cold. The women reached in little containers and hauled out what looked like jelly donuts. Trudy's was filled with cabbage and mine was filled with meat. It was not as good as a piece of pizza but it was hot and different. We traded. I gave her the meat and I took the cabbage. This was a *piroshki*.

As we watched the people and looked in the shop windows, we got so hungry we could have eaten a piroshki on every corner.

"We're so stupid, Rachel," Trudy exclaimed. "What are the basic human drives? The most elemental urges in life? Food, sex and booze. And what else?"

"Gambling, I guess," I said.

"Right. That's what three-for-one was talking about. We almost picked up a Bolshevik bookie."

The Christmas tree in the square opposite the Kremlin looked large enough from a distance. When we got closer to it it was absolutely colossal. It had a huge red star on top, almost as big as the one on the Kremlin Tower, and thousands of lights. Around the bottom was a ring of tiny decorated trees. Scores of young people held hands and danced around the tree singing and chanting. We stood there wondering how to cut in and join the group when a young man wandered over in our direction. He looked familiar. When we saw his gold tooth gleaming through his frosty breath, there was no mistaking. It was our old friend from this morning. Or his twin brother. Our Bolshevik bookie.

"We're being followed," Trudy said.

"He's not following us. He's lying in wait. Ambush."

"Nice American girls," he smiled. "I like doing business with Americans. I shook President Nixon's hand. I drank Pepsi Cola with him."

"Yes," we said. "You told us."

"You want to do business? Three for one?"

"We don't gamble," I said.

"Who said anything about gambling? Is no gamble. You no trust me?"

"We don't even know you."

"You don't have to drink with me to do business. I give you three for one. I told you."

"Three of what for one of what?" Trudy asked sharply.

He laughed. "I have rubles. You have dollars. You give me one dollar. I give you three rubles. At the Metropol you only get one. Do business with me, you buy three times as much vodka. Three times as much caviar. Good, no?"

"Black market!" we gasped. We'd been told about this but we thought it was a *place* like East Village in New York or Pigalle in Paris. We never thought of it as a man on the street.

"You're running a black market," Trudy said, acting shocked.

"You dig it, pooseykat," he said. "Roger. A-OK. Ready for business."

We noticed he was moving away from the crowd and reaching into his pockets, as if he were sure he was about to make a sale.

"That's what they give you thirty years for," I said to Trudy. "Let's get out of here."

"Thirty years for one dollar?" Suddenly the daring

of the whole encounter dawned on us. Moscow was very exciting. You merely walk to the corner and you have the opportunity to go to jail until 1999.

"We're very sorry," I explained. "But we are guests in your country. Your government has rules and we must obey them, whether we like it or not."

"That's right, pooseykat. Law and order. Tell me all about it. But if you know any swingers, tell them I give them three for one."

He was still smiling, with his one gold tooth shining through his misty breath in the light of the Red Star, as we retreated, like Napoleon, through the snows.

"He's terribly fresh, don't you think?" I said to Trudy.

"Yup," she said. "And cute, too."

*   *   *

After shopping for the better part of the following afternoon, we returned to the hotel and had a drink in the bar. We were politely joined by three young men, two of them Canadian, and one Russian. The Canadians came over first, asked if they could join us, and did. The Russian fellow, a good-looking man, came over to the table shortly thereafter. He introduced himself as Igor, a poet, and indicated he spoke fairly good English. We invited him to sit down.

Trudy seemed to have captivated the Canadians and it seemed I had won the interest of Igor. We talked a few minutes about Moscow and my reactions to it. Igor offered some interesting observations about his city and its people, none of them political and all presented low-key and without attempt to persuade. In fact, Igor seemed especially calm and subdued for a Russian. That's why his next statement took me by surprise.

"You will come with me," he said commandingly. It was an invitation couched as a kind of order.

"My friend and I were going to the Bolshoi," I told him.

"Which friend?" he wanted to know, casing the other two men at the table and frowning.

"My girl friend," I said.

"Oh," he said, breaking into a smile. Then he began talking Russian at a furious rate of speed to the Canadians. He was fast and effective, because in no time at all, one of the Canadians had invited Trudy to go to a party with *him*. Trudy explained she already had a date with me and we had to go into a huddle to clear all wires about going our separate routes.

"Where is he taking you?" Trudy wanted to know, when she finally got the message. "He might be an agent of the NKVD or another black marketeer or something and I might never see you again."

"I could be a spy, too, for all he knows. This suspicion business has to stop somewhere," I said.

"Well, he *is* good-looking," Trudy admitted. "I hope you know what you're doing."

When we walked out of the hotel it was a crystal-clear twenty below zero. Stepping into that kind of cold is like being thrown into an ice cold pool. At first you gasp for breath and think you're drowning. Gradually you discover you're not dead, you can feel yourself breathing, your head is in a perpetual cloud of steam. Then you have this furious urge to keep moving for fear you'll freeze. We put Trudy and her Canadian date into the first cab to whip over to the Bolshoi. I thought I'd freeze jumping around waiting for another cab, when Igor said, "We'll walk. It's only a little way."

"Walk?" I gasped, as astonished as if he had proposed a midnight swim.

"Is not too cold for you?" he said, giving me a big

Russian bear hug. It began to look like a Russian-American Olympics and I felt I couldn't let my country down. At least I had to try. Once I got moving, I was all right except for my hands. My heavy winter gloves were useless. Igor showed me how to clap my hands as we walked along, then hide them in my pockets. I had a heavy fur coat on, winter woolies and boots. He wore nothing but a short leather coat and a fur hat. For the first couple of blocks he didn't even bother to pull down his ear muffs.

"Are we getting there?" I asked, half dead with the cold.

"It's only a little way," he kept saying, the way he had in the beginning. We passed scores of people in the streets, promenading as if it were Fifth Avenue at Easter time.

"You should drink more vodka," Igor said.

I suggested we stop at a quiet neighborhood bar and refuel. He didn't seem to understand what I was saying. Then I realized he was probably very poor. Poets usually are. Maybe he didn't have the price of a taxi ride or was out of drinking money. I hated to sound like a rich capitalist lady, but I proposed we stop for a drink on me. He didn't understand me at all. I discovered later there is no such thing as a neighborhood bar. There are no saloons in Russia. You can get booze in restaurants and hotels and stores. But there are no public places where you can go and get stoned. The government discourages all that.

We had walked a good half mile when I saw a huge cloud of steam over the hill and the sounds of splashing water and people at play. The sound got clearer and more persistent so I asked about it.

"Oh," Igor said casually, "That's the swimming pool on Kropotkinskaya Ploshchad."

"A swimming pool outdoors?" I couldn't believe it.

"The water is heated. You want to go see?"

"No, thanks," I said. "I'll take your word for it."

Catching this bizarre sight at close range might have meant walking a few extra blocks. I had to conserve whatever energy I had left. We continued walking.

"We made very good speed," Igor said a few minutes later. "It is only a little way." I was ready to fall down but he pulled me along. Just as we found shelter in an apartment doorway, he spied an old tree with its trunk encrusted with snow. He dragged my freezing form over to look at it.

"This. I need the English word for this," he said. "You know?" He was lost in admiration of the crystalline formation on the tree trunk.

I didn't see it quite the way he did. "Ice?" I suggested, through clenched teeth.

"No, no." He shook his head. "I search for a word beautiful as this. An English word—for my poem."

"Get me a drink and I'll think about it," I promised.

We entered the hallway of a huge apartment building, ancient, drafty and strange. But once the door was opened to one of the flats, there was warmth and laughter and music. There must have been twenty people seated at a long improvised table that extended through two connecting rooms. The table was laden with food. The smells were strange and potent. A hefty, plainly-dressed woman with old-fashioned bobbed hair took our coats and our boots and found a place for us at the table. Nobody spoke English except Igor, but there was no mistaking the hospitality. The women really looked me over, examining every seam in the friendliest way. Igor introduced me *en masse* and I could only make out one word: *Amerikanski*. Everybody beamed and immediately they hoisted an incomprehensible toast to me. I smiled and replied as best I could, impatient to down whatever it was they put in my glass. It had a strange cool taste and a faint purple color. Igor explained it was vodka with pomegranate juice. It was like the mildest

Hawaiian Punch—with a kick like a mule. There was no ice in evidence and I didn't miss it for an instant. Older women kept coming in from the steaming kitchen carrying fresh bottles of vodka which were kept outside until chilled to a milky white, syrupy consistency. The food was endless. Fourteen kinds of antipasto. When I'd eaten my fill and thought I couldn't touch another bite, in came the main courses, steaming boiled fish with potatoes, beef stroganoff and chicken. Piles of black bread and six kinds of smoked herring and pickled mushrooms and smoked salmon that melted in my mouth. It seemed to be a marathon cooperative meal. People finished eating, drank toasts to the hosts and then departed. Others arrived to take their places. I couldn't tell the hosts from the guests. Everything seemed to be in unlimited supply. I looked around the room and spotted the huge grand piano in a corner of the room. Atop it were at least fifteen kinds of cakes, pies, cookies, and pastries. It looked gorgeous, but the thought of eating anything else was sickening.

I pushed back from the table and smiled at everyone. Since I couldn't speak the language, smiling was all I could do. Igor was too busy chattering up a storm to help me out as interpreter. Finally, one of the older women dragged a shy teen-aged girl to me and made an introduction.

"Please," the girl said to me, "I don't want to bother, but I must speak to you." The other guests looked at her and beamed.

"Not at all. I'm happy to meet you. You speak wonderful English."

"No." She blushed. "I study hard but my mother doesn't believe I really speak English. She wanted to see me talking to an American. I have to prove I can do it." All conversation stopped, and all eyes were on us.

"You tell your mother I said you speak excellent English."

"Thank you," she said.

"Can't you stay and be my interpreter?" I asked her.

The embarrassed child was thrilled at the suggestion. She reported it to her mother. There was applause. She became not my interpreter, but theirs. All the women crowded around me, asking questions. It got to be a real press conference about clothes, jobs, children, writing, travel and education. I was surrounded. They seemed delighted and impressed that I traveled all over the world, that I visited Moscow alone, that I had allegedly written a book. As women, they were proud that the first American they got to talk to was a *woman*. That seemed important to them.

Finally, Igor rescued me. He announced that we had to advance to the house of his friend, Eugen, a painter.

"How far do I have to walk?" I asked him.

"Little way," he answered.

I had to kiss about thirty people twice on each cheek and then we were off into the Russian winter. I didn't realize how drunk I was until the wind hit me. This time, I braved it like a real Muscovite. I felt I could have walked to Leningrad. Igor was feeling no pain, either. He hung onto my hips and began singing up a storm. The street was dark and quiet, and after only a few blocks, we entered a small, three-storey building huddled between two ancient structures that looked like palaces. I was staggering a little, half from the vodka and half from the cold. When I started limping up the inevitable stairs, Igor picked me up, threw me over his shoulder and started carrying me, leaping up two or three steps at a time. It was a formidable display of masculinity and absolutely the first time I was ever carried over anybody's threshold.

He shouted a sharp Russian command to Eugen and they conducted me to a mattress on the floor in the corner of a cluttered room.

"This is Rachel Jones, Eugen. Give her vodka!"

We drank and watched the snow fall on Moscow through the one large window in Eugen's studio. It was a beautiful sight, one I'll never forget. The room was comfortable, although not overheated.

"Moscow is beautiful like this," Igor said sadly, just like a Russian in a movie.

I agreed.

"I would like so much to live here," he lamented.

"I thought you did."

"No," he whispered. "I cannot get permission." Then he explained that Moscow is Mecca for many young Russians, but to live there requires government permission. You have to prove yourself necessary to the political, economic or cultural life of the capital.

The studio was small and cluttered. Igor, Eugen and I shared the same pad on the floor. The shortage of space forced an instant kind of intimacy, but where does one go when one wants to be alone? Love in a cold climate presents certain problems. Necking in cars and taxis is strictly out. You could freeze to death. Necking in the street is impossible. Any love-making at home is apt to be inhibited by the presence of mother, brothers, sisters, or friends. So what do you do? I guess you drink. I could easily see why Russians drank too much and why the government did all it could to stem the tide of alcoholism in Russia.

After a few more vodkas, Eugen put a record on a small record player. It was jazz—Bill Evans. Eugen had other American jazz records, too, smuggled in by friends. I promised him a Theolonius Monk record on my next visit. We celebrated my promise with another vodka. Then I began to wonder about the hour. It was getting late and I had to be thinking about getting back to the hotel. When I asked Igor about telephoning for a taxi, he poured me another vodka and explained that Eugen did not rate a telephone.

"What are we going to do?" I asked helplessly.

"Don't worry," said Igor. "Eugen goes. He brings back a taxi."

"I hate to be so much trouble," I apologized.

"Is nothing," said Igor.

Before he left, Eugen fortified himself with a couple more drinks. Of course, we had to join him in a toast, with Igor doing the honors. We drank once to America and once to Russia and then Igor got very solemn.

"The Soviet Union prepared for war with the United States," Igor said. "The United States prepared for war with the Soviet Union. It does not happen. We drink to what does not happen."

I wanted another vodka like I wanted to go swimming in the outdoor pool on the Kropotkinskaya Ploschchad, but I *had* to drink to that.

Eugen left to find the taxi.

It was getting cold in the studio so I slipped into my fur coat. Igor got very mournful at the prospect of my having to leave and sat down on the mattress in the corner beside me. He held my hand and described the encrusted snows on the bark of the birch trees. He insisted there must be a perfect English word for it.

"Yes, Igor," I kept saying. "I'm thinking about it."

I don't know how I sensed it was morning. It was dark as midnight through the window when I woke up, but something told me I had been sleeping a good while. Igor was snoring peacefully beside me with his arm over my thigh. It was ten twenty, if my watch could be believed. Trudy would be climbing the walls with worry about me. And where was Eugen with his taxi? I knew where *I* ought to be, but I didn't know where I was.

I shook Igor and punched him and shook him some more. He remained asleep. In desperation, I began stroking his chin and tickling him under the nose.

Suddenly, he jolted to a sitting position, looked around and embraced me. "You have it?" he bellowed. "You remembered the word!"

"Not exactly," I said. "I remembered I have an English-Russian dictionary back at the hotel. That's what we need."

"Is good one?" he asked.

"Very good," I said. "Excellent, in fact."

He was on his feet in a minute, ready to light the fire to make tea. "No, no," I said, "we'll have tea at the hotel. Let's get a taxi."

The streets were teeming with people. Old women were at work with their brooms collecting the new snow into neat little piles. We walked halfway to the hotel before Igor finally hailed a taxi. It refused to stop for us and we had to get into line in a taxi queue a block away. It was so cold standing there after 30 seconds I was ready to walk, skip or jump—anything to keep moving. I was frozen stiff by the time we got within sight of the Metropol.

I asked Igor to wait in the lobby while I ran upstairs. The lady concierge in the hall smiled at me knowingly as I picked up the key. The room was still dark when I let myself in. Miss Baker was sleeping as peacefully as a kitten under piles of Russian quilts. As quietly as I could manage in the darkness, I began rummaging through my bag.

"What time is it, Rach?" she chirped.

"Almost noon," I said. "How long have you been sleeping?"

"About ten or fifteen minutes."

"Ten *minutes?*"

"I wanted to call you so you wouldn't worry, but I was too stoned."

"What were you drinking—vodka with pomegranate juice?"

"Sort of purple?"

"Yeah, that's powerful stuff. Powerful. What happened?"

"I wish I knew," she said. "What happened at your party?"

"We'll talk about it later. You go ahead and sleep it off," I suggested.

I found the dictionary and trotted down to the lobby and presented it to Igor. He was crushed. He already *had* a copy, and it was no help at all.

I thanked him for a beautiful evening and promised to bring back some more English books on my next trip. I promised to keep brooding in search of the word. But if I uncovered a possibility, how could I find him?

"You must send it to Eugen. He can find me," he said.

"I'm sorry *we* didn't find it," I said. "I tried. But it just didn't happen. Did it?"

He kissed me on both cheeks and left.

CHAPTER VIII

"I Don't Care What The Song Says, Get Out of My Tent!"

The airline industry, like all other industries, spawns its own particular brand of myth and rumor. These myths, once started, grow in form and content until it's difficult to ferret out the real facts surrounding them. It's like passing the joke along a line of people, each telling his own version in a foreign language. What comes out at the end bears little resemblance to the original.

One such myth of stewardessing involves Jane Middleton. She'd flown for our airline a few years before we arrived. In fact, she'd flown for five airlines. As this tale begins, Jane had taken employment with her sixth airline, a tiny Arab line serving off-beat airports in remote regions of the Arab world. You see, Jane Middleton was a great gal, full of bounce and fun. She was also one of the prize foul-ups of the stewardess business, thus her journeyman career.

Jane's unforgettable experience while flying for the Arab airline has been told and retold throughout the world. Obviously the basic situation did occur. We've tried to gather together all the available versions of the story in order that we could relate the tale to you in this book.

*   *   *

Yashid Nastush looked up from his camel and saw the DC-6 drone over his head. "Big bird," he muttered.

"No, stupid," Shaloom Nashtush answered. "It's an airplane."

The two Arab Bedouin brothers watched the plane disappear into a swirling, yellow haze of windswept sand. Inside the aircraft, the two members of the cockpit crew were fighting to keep the plane under control. Old, and with too many hours in its flight log, the DC-6 had suddenly begun to pull sharply to the left, despite the efforts of the crew. One of four such aircraft in the fleet of a small, Arabian airline, the DC-6 was on a scheduled trip between Damascus, Syria, and Riyadh, Saudi Arabia.

The pilot, a Britisher tanned to an African hue, fought the controls while his co-pilot, an Arab trained in England, scrambled out of his seat, kneeled on the cockpit floor and faced east.

"Bloody fool," Captain Sterling cursed as he held the aircraft in a tight, strained circle to the right. "Get up in your bloody seat and help me fly this bloody airplane." His co-pilot climbed back into his seat, still mumbling prayers.

In the rear of the aircraft, seven passengers, all Arabs, sensed the difficulty and grabbed tightly to the armrests. The flight's only stewardess stumbled up the aisle and opened the cockpit door.

"We're losing control," Captain Sterling yelled at her. "Prepare everyone for a bloody crash landing."

"Yes, sir," the stewardess answered, closing the door and returning to the passenger compartment. This stew was Jane Middleton. She cursed the DC-6 and strapped herself into her seat. Securely belted in, she yelled at the passengers, "Tighten your seat belts, get your glasses off, put a pillow on your laps and hold on. We're crashing." There was a loud moan from the passengers, but Jane ignored it. "I should have given up flying and taken that saleslady's job," she grumbled, watching the yellow desert come up to meet them.

Captain Sterling held the plane off the surface of the desert for what seemed an eternity, and then allowed it to settle onto the sand. The wheels sunk in, but not deep enough to cause the aircraft to nose over. It eventually came to a stop halfway up the side of a large sand dune.

"How's that for a bloody neat crash landing?" Captain Sterling said to his co-pilot. His cockpit crew member was too shaken to respond. He just sat there and said prayers to the east, which necessitated turning his head completely around. Sterling shrugged, unbuckled himself and went back to the passenger compartment. The passengers were up milling around. Jane Middleton was still in her seat, a nettled expression on her pretty face.

"How come you went up the hill?" she asked Captain Sterling.

"Well, my dear, I really didn't have very much of a bloody choice in the matter."

Jane grunted, unstrapped herself and got up. She opened the door and looked out over the endless expanse of desert. The heat came through the door in a blast; it was at least 120 degrees. She closed the door and yelled to Captain Sterling to put the air conditioning back on.

"Can't do that, love. I don't want to wear down the batteries. They're as old as the bloody plane, you know."

"How long will we be here, Captain?" a well-spoken Arab gentleman asked.

"Can't really tell, old chap. I managed to radio the nearest oil drilling facility and told them we were going down. I suppose they'll arrange to send one of their bloody pipeline inspection planes over soon enough. At least, let's hope they do." Sterling laughed grimly.

The plane heated up rapidly. Soon, the inside of the

passenger compartment was insufferable. Jane kicked open the door and everyone exited. They gathered in the aircraft's shade and waited silently, their eyes trained on the yellow, sandy air for signs of a rescue aircraft.

Night began to fall and still they sat, their eyes to the heavens. Had they looked across the desert on the other side of the plane, they would have seen the Bedouin party led by Yashid and Shaloom. There were eleven Arabs in all. They led six camels in single file.

"Look!" Yashid exclaimed, spotting the downed DC-6. "Big bird come down."

"I've already told you it's not a big bird, dum-dum," Shaloom snapped. "It's an airplane and it carries people." Ever since Shaloom returned from two years' schooling in Beirut, he was impossible to live with. He flaunted his new education at every turn, which infuriated his fellow-Bedouins. Shaloom didn't care how they felt. He wanted only to leave the Bedouin life and take a job in an air-conditioned office in the city. But the code of his tribe dictated that he return and share his knowledge gained at the university. "Two years of computer science and I have to hang with dopes who think airplanes are birds," he mumbled, jerking his camel to attention. The camel snarled and spit at Shaloom. He kicked the camel in the leg and thought of the air-conditioned Ford he used to drive in Beirut.

The Bedouin party was under the DC-6's other wing before anyone noticed them. It was Captain Sterling who spotted the Arabs and their camels.

"Blimey, the bloody savages have arrived.

"Hi ho, everybody," Sterling said. "We people, like you. Come down here in bloody big bird." He pointed to the DC-6. Yashid looked at Shaloom and sneered.

"I speak English," Shaloom said.

"Good show, mate. I'm Captain Clarence Sterling, airline pilot. I'm your friend. I even flew with you in Algeria against those blasted French. Picked up a little loose change in those days."

Shaloom approached Captain Sterling and smiled.

"How's tricks?" he asked, flashing a grin accented by two gold teeth in front.

"How's tricks? Where'd you learn that bloody Yank expression?"

"Beirut. At the University. I studied with an American teacher."

Sterling and Shaloom engaged in an animated and spirited conversation. Sterling gave the Arab a cigarette, and the Arab slapped Sterling on the back and they bantered back and forth while everyone else looked on. Everyone, that is, except Yashid Nastush. He gathered the other Arabs around him and launched into an equally animated conversation. The subject of their interest was Jane Middleton, who stood beside the flight's co-pilot. With all eyes trained on Sterling and Shaloom, no one noticed Yashid lead the other Bedouins towards Jane. Without warning, they pounced, picked her up and ran towards the camels.

"I say, put the bloody girl down," Sterling yelled. Shaloom screamed something in Arabic, but neither protest stopped the Arabs. They threw Jane on the ground and formed a circle around her. Each man drew a long, curved knife and stood firm, fierce determination fixed on their faces.

"What's this all about?" Sterling asked Shaloom. Shaloom shrugged and walked to Yashid. He asked the same question in Arabic. Yashid answered by telling Shaloom he was going to deliver Jane to their father and chieftain, Ibn "Sweet Lips" Nastush. "This will be the great prize for our father," Yashid told Shaloom. "I will be favored son. You will no longer be favorite because you go away to learn." Shaloom argued with his brother, but to no avail. In fact, Yashid turned his knife on his educated brother and commanded him to mount his camel. Jane lay sprawled in the sand, a terrified look on her pretty, pale face. Two Bedouins pulled her to her feet, slung her across a camel, and the band disappeared into the night.

"I say, come back here, you bloody thieves," Sterling shouted. His words drifted back to him in the gusty desert wind.

"Well, this is a fine kettle of fish and chips, isn't it?" he said. "I wonder what they'll bloody do with her."

"It depends," the well-spoken Arab passenger answered. "If the Bedouin chief is pleased with her, she will go into his harem and serve him sexually for the rest of her young life. If he is displeased, he will put her to death."

"I rather imagine he'll like her, don't you, old chap?"

"It's hard to forecast the mind of a desert chieftain, Captain Sterling. It is written that the desert wind fans the sexual flames of desert warriors. Pretty, pale stewardess will be called upon for much pleasure. The question is whether she is capable of giving so much pleasure. Is she, Captain Sterling?"

"You know, I don't really know. I've never really had her, if you know what I mean. Oh, we've petted a little and swam nude once, but . . . Why in blazes am I talking like this?"

"The mind of man sometimes lags behind the tongue of man, captain. It is written."

"Yes. Well, we'd better put our bloody minds to the task of rescuing poor Jane from the hands of those filthy savages." The Arab passenger registered his displeasure at the captain's terminology and walked back to the others.

The Bedouin tribe traveled throughout the night. Jane was bounced and buffeted aboard the camel until she thought she would split in two. Shaloom was treated as a prisoner by his brother.

"When I tell Daddy about this," Shaloom said, "he'll cut your unworthy tongue out." His brother just grinned and looked at Jane.

"When our father sees what Yashid has brought him, he will reward me."

"Help!" Jane chirped, more out of habit than conviction. She called for help every quarter of a mile, which made the Bedouins laugh.

The sun was beginning to rise as the Bedouin party came over a hill and swept down into their camp. Jane squinted through the blowing sand and surveyed the camp, a circle of tents dominated by one large tent at the far end. Fires burned in the middle of the circle; Arabs slept near the fire. Yashid yelped a notice of their arrival and the Arabs around the fires leaped up and ran to greet them. Yashid grabbed the rope around Jane's camel and proudly led her on an inspection tour of the camp. The others ran behind, jabbering about the pale girl and Yashid's apparent conquest. It was a festive atmosphere until the flap to the big tent was thrown open and Ibn Nastush, grand chieftain of the tribe, walked into the clearing. He shouted something in Arabic and everyone fell silent, including Yashid.

"Help," Jane said weakly.

Ibn Nastush clapped his hands together and everyone scattered, leaving Yashid, Shaloom and Jane in the circle.

"Your ding-a-ling son and my jerky brother has done a grave thing, Daddy," Shaloom said, jumping down from his camel.

"No, Father," Yashid protested. "I have brought you a fair pale maiden from the desert. A great

bird descended from the sky and brought her to us.
I bring her home for you, honored father and chieftain of our humble tribe."

Jane was terrified. The chief was a horrible looking man. He weighed three hundred pounds. His face
was thick and wrinkled. A long, flowing beard and
moustache sprouted from his face and blew with
abandon in the morning breeze. But what was particularly upsetting was his mouth. It was fixed in a
sinister, downward position, the ends reaching to the
jawline, the middle portion fleshy and red. And there
were knives hanging from his sash, three long, curved
weapons with jeweled handles.

"Big bird bring pale girl?" the chief asked Yashid.

"It wasn't a bird, Daddy. It was an airplane, a
DC-6, piloted by a British officer named Sterling."

"Yes. Yashid is not blessed with the wisdom of
you, my educated son. Birds do not bring pale ladies
to the desert."

Yashid looked hurt. Shaloom sensed his superiority
of the moment, and pressed his advantage.

"Daddy, Yashid has done a bad thing. He has
kidnapped this girl. Soon, the desert will be swarming
with men looking for her. They will come and war
on us, Daddy."

"What is this kidnap, my son?"

"It is very bad, Daddy. A felony."

"Yes, you have erred, Yashid, my son. I have told
many times of my wishes, but you do not listen. I
feel there is much of a . . . a . . ."

"Gap, Daddy. It is called a generation gap."

"No matter what it is called. As much suffering as
you bring to me at times, Yashid, I must be proud of
your warrior mind and inclinations. You, Shaloom,
have lost much in gaining education. You have lost
courage and the adventure of our forefathers."

Ibn Nastush surveyed Jane on the camel. Her uni-

form had ridden up high on her thighs and her blouse
was open at the top, revealing the beginning of her
bosom. The chief allowed his black eyes to wander
over her. He looked at Shaloom. He looked at
Yashid. He looked again at Jane. "Bring the pale
girl in," he commanded. "I will decide this later, after
dinner." Jane kicked and screamed as Yashid pulled
her down from the camel, slung her over his shoulder
and carried her into the chief's tent. Yashid allowed
his hand to travel up her leg. Jane punched him in the
mouth. The young Arab warrior dropped her to the
ground and was about to kick her when his father
commanded him to leave the tent. He backed away.

"Take the pale girl to the other women of my
home," the father told Shaloom. "Tell them to prepare her for dinner."

Jane yelled louder than ever. "Nobody's eating
me," she screamed. The father laughed. "Away with
her." Shaloom took her by the arms and led her
through an interior flap. Once on the other side, he
shook her and whispered, "I am your friend. I will
protect you."

"Never mind protecting me," Jane said. "Just get
me out of here."

"Patience."

"Where are you taking me?"

"To the harem of my father. The wives there will
bathe you and make you pretty for dinner. My father
will dine with you alone. That is his custom with
new harem members."

"I'm not going to be in anybody's harem. Listen,
fella, I'm no prude, but no harem for me. Besides,
I think your old man is a fat pig."

"Sssshh, stewardess. Trust in me."

Shaloom took Jane to a room in the tent in which
more than a dozen Arab girls were lounging on silk
pillows. They jumped up as Shaloom entered and

surrounded him. It was obvious to Jane that each girl was anxious to claim Shaloom as a lover. She watched nervously as they tugged at his clothing and caressed his face and ran their fingers through his hair. But he put a stop to that and ordered that they make Jane ready for a special dinner that evening. The reaction was immediate and intense. The girls thought Jane was Shaloom's choice, and they turned black, hate-filled eyes on her. Jane started to ask Shaloom if he'd explain to them what was happening, but he quickly left the room, leaving Jane in the middle of the harem girls.

"Hi," she said.

They responded by making cat sounds and pulling her roughly to a big, tin bathtub against one of the tent walls. Two of the girls went to fetch water while two others began yanking Jane's clothes off.

"Hey, cut it out," she yelled, but no one listened. They had her stripped in seconds, and she suddenly felt very cold in the hundred degree heat of the tent. She looked around for something—anything—to put on, but there was nothing. All she could do was stand there, her arms folded across her ample breasts, one thigh in front of the other, and cringe as the the girls walked around and openly examined her nude figure. She tried to tell from the voices whether they approved or disapproved; she guessed they disapproved. One girl poked her in her stomach, another slapped her rear end, and still another pulled her arms down and flicked a nipple with her finger. All this handling stuck a hot poker of rage in Jane, and she lashed out, fists clenched, at the nearest girls. They scattered, picking up pillows as protection against this pale, female gladiator. Jane stopped swinging, looked around, walked to the tub which was now filled with hot water, and got in. "The hell with all of you," she proclaimed, settling into the relaxing warmth of the bath. One of the harem girls approached and offered soap. Jane smiled, pointed over her shoulder to indicate she'd like her back washed, and closed her eyes. The Arab girls began to slowly soap Jane's back. Neither of them noticed the knife pierce the tent wall immediately beside the tub. The blade sliced down slowly, creating a three-inch cut in the wall. Two fingers carefully parted the material to allow one black eye to peek through. It was Yashid. He feasted his gaze on Jane in the tub, and his heart began to pound. He took a deep breath, which was audible to Jane. She opened her eyes, looked sideways, saw what was happening, reached down, cupped some water in her hands and threw it at the hole. It caught Yashid in the eye. He sputtered and cursed and ran away. Jane stood up in the tub, and a harem girl came to her with a large cloth. Jane wrapped herself in it, smiled, and went with the girl to another corner of the room where two other girls waited to fix her hair. Jane marveled at herself as she settled down on silk cushions and allowed the Arab girls to fuss over her. In fact, she was beginning to enjoy this phase of captivity. But she knew there was more to come.

The pipe-line inspection plane, a Cessna 150, arrived at the scene of the DC-6's crash landing at about eight that morning. It made several passes over the area, dropped supplies, radioed Captain Sterling that another aircraft would arrive shortly, and flew away. At nine, the second plane arrived, a larger light plane with sand skids for landing on the desert. Its pilot, a scruffy young man, listened as Captain Sterling told of Jane's kidnapping.

"You know, old chap, these Arabs can be absolutely savage when it comes to a pretty western woman. I think we'd better make all possible haste to rescue the poor thing before this bloody chief of theirs sticks it to her, if you follow me."

The oil company pilot blew his nose between his

fingers and snorted. "Hell, don't worry about fat ol' Ibn Nastush. Hell, he's impotent." He pronounced it like important, which confused Sterling.

"Well, of course he's important, man. Any bloody chief is important."

"Not important, Mac. Impotent. You know, he can't make it no more with the broads."

"You're jolly well kidding."

"The hell I am. He's a fat old man who was booted out by his brothers at the palace. They gave him some losers for a tribe and sent him out to the desert. Hell, he ain't gonna do anything to your stewardess, unless he gets all mad and upset and kills her. He's done that before. You can't blame him, though, now can ya? After all, put yourself in that spot, huh? All them broads around and you can't do nothin' about it. Man, I'd be ready to kill anybody."

Sterling winced as he reflected on Jane's fate. He regretted not having become more intimate with her. If he knew she was proficient in love, he'd have felt more secure.

"How soon can you fly some men in here, old chap?" Sterling asked the oil company pilot.

"What for?"

"To rescue Jane, of course."

"Don't know. The only guys near here are the guys on the pipe line. Hell, I don't figure they'd wanna go chasin' after this here girl and all them Arabs. Man, they can be a mean bunch when they get riled up."

"I don't doubt that, old man, but something has to be done for poor Jane. You really don't think you could get your chums to go after her?"

"Nope."

"Hmmmm. Well, that leaves the bloody thing up to me. I am her captain, after all. Let me see. Suppose you fly me up to their camp, and you and I will take a fling at saving her."

"No, thanks. I got one more year to go on this job and a lot 'a loot stashed away back in Philly. I ain't blowin' it for no broad."

"Dastardly attitude, I must say. Well, how about flying me and my co-pilot up there and sort of dropping us off?"

"Yeah, I could do that. What about these here passengers?"

"Can you send for another bloody plane?"

"Yea. When d'ya wanna go?"

"Right now, old chap. Every minute we lose could mean disaster for poor old Jane."

The oil company pilot called his base to find that the other large aircraft had developed mechanical trouble. Captain Sterling decided, through clenched teeth, that his passengers would have to be evacuated in the plane at hand before he could attempt to rescue Jane. It took two trips to move the six passengers, and by the time the pilot had returned to pick up Sterling, it was four in the afternoon. The co-pilot had vehemently declined to assist in the rescue attempt, claiming that for him to war against his own people would certainly bring godly retribution in its most intense fury.

"Bloody coward," Sterling yelled after him as he made the second trip with the final three passengers. "Bloody boob." The co-pilot made an obscene Arab gesture from the plane's window and shouted a few things of his own. Captain Sterling waited alone until the oil company pilot returned with an empty plane.

"Remember now," the pilot told Sterling, "I'm gonna drop you off plenty far away from the camp. Remember that."

"Right-o, old chap. I read you loud and clear."

It took over an hour to reach the Bedouin camp. The pilot spotted it first, turned the aircraft into a slow, descending circle and settled down on a flat piece of desert, which was hidden from the camp by a large sand dune. Sterling lighted a cigarette and sat quietly. Perspiration dripped freely from his face.

"I say, old chap, it is frightfully hot out here, isn't it? This blasted desert could sweat a man to death."

The oil company pilot nodded.

"This bloody, hot cigarette doesn't help, either."

"Here, try one 'a mine. It's got menthol."

"Oh, that's mighty decent of you, old chap." Sterling accepted the cigarette from the pilot, and at the same time reached across and pulled the ignition key from the instrument panel.

"Hey, buddy, what the hell you think you're . . . ?"

"Just assuring us a way out of this infernal desert, old man." With that, Sterling pulled a snub-nosed revolver from his belt and held it on the pilot. "Now, I'm going to get out and remove something from your aircraft's engine, just to assure you don't go starting the craft without the bloody key. Then, I'm going into that bloody camp and rescue Jane. And then, my dear fellow, we're coming back here and you're going to fly us away to safety in your plane. Is that clear?"

"I ain't got no choice."

"Good thinking, old chap. By the way, have you a gun?"

"Yeah. Behind the seat." The pilot realized he shouldn't have answered. Sterling reached behind the seat and came up with a sawed-off shotgun.

"Nasty looking weapon, I must say," he muttered. "Could I convince you to join me on this expedition, old chap? I could use a second hand, and gun."

"Drop dead. I ain't going near that bunch 'a savages."

"Yes. Well, I'll simply have to take both weapons, one in each hand, and juggle best I can. I'll be back sometime after dark. I trust you'll be here?"

"Yeah, I'll be here. Just make sure you got plenty 'a distance between you and those nuts."

"Right-o."

Sterling exited the plane, opened the engine cowling and removed something. He put it in the pocket of his tan bush jacket, pushed his fifty-mission airline pilot's hat down tightly on his head and headed in the direction of the large dune. He turned after fifty yards and yelled back, "You sure you won't join me, old chap?"

"Drop dead."

"I wish you wouldn't say that. It bloody well gives me shivers."

Sterling went to the crest of the dune, laid down and looked over on to the Bedouin camp. Night was falling, and the fires in the circle of tents were being relighted. He looked back and saw the oil company pilot sitting on top of the plane.

"Bugger," Sterling whispered to himself. "No honor left in the world."

Sterling waited until darkness was complete. He'd surmised that the large tent was probably that of the chief, and would be where Jane was being held captive. He checked his watch: 8:15. "I'll give it until nine," he said, scratching where sand fleas had bitten him on his lower legs.

As Captain Clarence Sterling lay on the sand dune, Jane Middleton was led to the chief's main chamber. The harem girls had dressed her in their finest silk. A flowing veil covered the lower half of her face. Gold and silver rings had been placed on eight fingers, with an extra one adorning the big toe on her right foot. She'd been doused in perfume. She looked and felt very much the harem princess.

"Welcome, pale girl from the sky," Ibn Nastush said from his throne of two hundred pillows. Two huge Africans fanned the ruler with palm fronds, while a teen-aged Arab girl massaged his feet. He clapped his hands and the girl backed from the chamber. "Sit," he commanded, patting some pillows next to him. Jane approached, patted the pillows with her hand and plopped down.

Ibn Nashtush clapped again. Two of the harem girls came through a curtain and began to dance to music originating from behind another curtain. They swirled and twirled in front of the chief and his captive, hands above their heads, tiny finger cymbals pinging in rhythm to the dissonant music. It was all very enjoyable for Jane. Once, in Boston, she'd visited the Club Zara, but the authenticity of the harem dancers surpassed the nightclub belly dancers. She even found herself clapping to the music. The chief seemed pleased at her pleasure and began clapping, too. He stomped his big bare feet and grinned and weaved back and forth on his throne.

The dancing completed, Ibn ordered dinner be served. Jane watched with interest as slaves brought trays brimming with food. Jane looked down at what was the first course and peered into a clear, thin soup. Peering back at her were two eyes, perfectly round and white with the black iris and retina set in an inquisitive stare.

"What's that?" she yelped.

"It is lamb soup. Do not eat the eye of the lamb until you have enjoyed the broth."

A swell of nausea filled Jane's stomach, and she pushed the bowl away. "I can't eat somebody's eyes."

"Very strange," Ibn Nastush said. "It is written that the eye of the lamb brings inner vision to the eater of the eye. No matter. Perhaps you would prefer the testicles."

"I want a rare hamburger."

"What is this hamburger?"

"Forget it. It is written that hamburgers sit better on a stewardess's stomach."

"Very strange."

More food was brought. Jane tasted most of the dishes, but nibbled only sparingly. When dinner was finished, everyone vacated the chamber, leaving Jane and Ibn Nastush alone. He belched a number of times, wiped the grease into his beard with the back of his hand, and turned his deep, black eyes on Jane.

"It is time now for you as my newest wife to perform her duties to Ibn Nastush. Disrobe, please."

"I wanted to talk to you about that, chief. I love eating with you and the floorshow was great, but I really don't feel in the mood to make love. Do you understand?" The chief answered by bellowing and clapping his hands. Two of the harem girls appeared and came to Jane's feet. Ibn uttered a garbled order and the girls reached up to begin undressing her. She fought. The chief clapped his hands again and the two African palm frond fanners reappeared, grabbed Jane's arms and held her while the girls worked on stripping away the silk garments. Ibn picked his teeth and hummed an old Arabian lullaby as this went on.

Captain Sterling began approaching the camp at nine. His wait on the dune's crest had resulted in what seemed to be 500 flea bites. The itching was unbearable, and slowed him up as he was forced to stop and scratch. "Bloody little bastards," he mumbled, digging into a particularly nasty bite. He circled around to the rear of the large tent, lay still for a few minutes to make sure no one was in the area, and carefully crawled towards the rear wall. Upon reaching it, and after scratching many bites, he took a penknife from his pocket and carefully sliced a small slit in the tent. He peered inside. He saw nothing but two Arab boys cleaning dishes. He crawled

around to another side of the tent and was surprised
to find a slit already in the wall. He peeked in. The
harem girls were bathing. Never in Sterling's travels
had he seen so many naked women in one place. He
watched as two of the girls climbed into the tin tub
directly in front of him and started soaping each
other. But then he remembered Jane, poor Jane, and
tore himself away. He moved to another side of the
tent. He was turning the corner on all fours when he
spotted the figure of another man, crouched in the
darkness, his eye pressed against the tent. "What's
this rogue up to?" he wondered, advancing on the
figure. Sterling came up behind, drew back his revolver and brought the handle down hard on the
man's neck. The figure slumped, and leaned to the
right. Then it collapsed on the sand without a sound.
Sterling looked down and recognized the face as one
of the two Bedouin brothers who'd kidnapped Jane.
It was Yashid. Sterling peered through the slit. He
gasped as he looked into Ibn Nastush's chambers.
There was Jane, nude, held taut by two giant black
warriors. Ibn Nastush had undressed and was parad-
ing in front of her.

"Bloody exhibitionist," Sterling said, taking a tight
hold on his revolver and shotgun.

The naked chief clapped his hands and the black
warriors let go of Jane's arms and disappeared from
Sterling's view.

The chief looked down. He had trouble seeing below
his massive stomach, but eventually his gaze cleared
the blubber. He smiled. He laughed. He clapped his
hands like a child and began pirouetting about the
tent chamber like an elephant in ballet class.

"I am a man again," he cried, stopping his dance
in front of Jane. "You and your lovely pale body
from the sky has made me a man again. I decree,
and so shall it be, that you shall forever be number

one wife of Ibn Nastush. I decree that all others of my tribe shall kneel before you. I decree that all my wealth shall be yours to share. I decree these things, and so it shall be." The chief advanced on Jane, arms outstretched in a gesture of love.

"Not by a long shot, you fat, uncivilized bloody lecher." Sterling sliced the tent wall to the ground and leaped through the opening.

"Clarence!"

"Jane!"

Ibn's body shook with rage. He yelled for his guards.

"Come on, Jane," Sterling said. "Grab your bloody clothes and come with me." Jane grabbed the silk garments worn earlier in the evening, took Sterling's hand and went with him through the tent opening. Yashid had just gotten up from the ground as the couple came through. Sterling punched him in the nose, sending him sprawling in the sand. "Come on, girl, we haven't a moment to waste."

"Can't I get dressed, first?" she asked.

"No, of course not. Oh, all right. These damn fleas will just eat you up if you don't." Clarence scratched his own bites while Jane slipped into her outfit. They took off on the run. Behind them, twenty Bedouins took up the chase.

"Get them, get them!" Ibn Nastush screamed from his tent.

Sterling and Jane raced along the back wall of tents and cut out for the dune. They scrambled up the slope, slipping and sliding in the loose sand. Once at the crest, they looked back and saw the Bedouins charging towards the dune, long, curved swords drawn and glimmering menacingly in the moonlight.

"Come on, girl," Sterling urged.

"I've got to scratch."

They both scratched. Then they raced down the

other side of the dune. The oil company pilot was asleep on the wing. "Wake up, you bloody fool," Sterling yelled, opening the cowling and replacing the engine part.

"Hurry, Clarence," Jane pleaded from the cockpit. Sterling slammed the cowling shut, jumped in beside her and handed the pilot the aircraft keys. The engine roared to life and the plane began to move along the sand. It picked up speed and left the ground amidst a barrage of thrown swords. They clanked off the aircraft's sides; the propeller actually tossed one a hundred feet into the air. Below, the Bedouins screamed and cursed and shook their fists.

"Bloody close scrape, hey?" Sterling said, lighting a cigarette.

"Oh, yes," Jane sighed, snuggling against him.

"I'm sure you didn't count on this sort of bloody nonsense when you signed on as a stewardess with the line."

"I sure didn't, Clarence."

"Jane?"

"Yes."

"Did he violate you in any way?"

"The chief?"

"Yes."

"No. Actually, I feel sort of sorry for him."

"Don't talk that way. He's a bloody savage."

"I know. But he does have a hang up. I'm kind of glad I helped him a little."

"Will you fly again, Jane?"

"No, I don't think so. I have a job offered me at Bloomingdale's in New York. The sweater department. I think I'll go back and take it. Maybe I'll meet a nice guy looking for a cardigan and marry him."

"Jane?"

"What?"

"Would you consider me?"

"For what, Clarence?"

"As a husband."

"I couldn't, Clarence. I could never bear to think of you flying here in the desert with all these dangers and risks."

"I won't fly any more, Jane. As a matter of fact, I have a brother who works at N. Peal in London. He's always after me to go to work there in sporting goods. I'm sure he could place you in sweaters. We could make a go of it, Jane. I know bloody well we could."

"I'd love to try, Clarence."

"Good show."

*　　*　　*

A year later, a wandering horde of Bedouins attacked Ibn Nastush's camp and slaughtered everyone, including the chief and his wives. The story was carried across the desert that when the bodies were found, Ibn Nastush was discovered clinging to a tattered, dirty airline stewardess's uniform. His son, Shaloom, the only member of the tribe who escaped death by reason of his employment with IBM in Beirut, was asked to explain the uniform.

"It is written," he said, "that once a large, silver bird came down from the heavens and deposited a pale, lovely lady in the desert. She wore the uniform of the sky and performed a great service for my father. Of course, this is all desert legend and all of us now know such things do not happen. But my father was a lover of legends. In fact, he was a lover in all ways. Excuse me, please. I must attend to some changes in the data imputs."

CHAPTER IX

"Maryanne's Baby"

All the American refugees in Sweden aren't GI deserters from Vietnam. Some of them are airline stewardesses, wounded in action, so to speak. We know at least two of them who found refuge there. One of them is Maryanne, and thereby hangs a tale.

Actually we knew her roomate Gail better than we knew Maryanne. We had both worked with Gail and one night, when she begged us to come over for an impromptu stew-zoo beer and pizza party, we begged off. We were beat. But when Gail kept insisting, we knew something was up. We dragged our weary bodies down.

The beer revived us somewhat and the pizza was better than usual. Which was more than you could say for the conversation. Gail was about as subtle as a kick in the teeth. She kept steering the seminar back to the subject of the pill vs. the coil, the diaphragm vs. the pill, the stupidity of American abortion laws. You wouldn't have to be a regular listener to the afternoon TV soap operas to know somebody was pregnant and this was a group therapy session to get the subject out into the open, to discuss it rationally and to help somebody there understand she did have friends in time of need.

None of the other stews had anything to say on the subject that you could call brilliant.

"I know what I'd do," a busty southern Delta girl said. "I'd get myself a good doctor and take care of it in a hurry."

There were arguments about whether you could trust

the doctors in New York. There were arguments about
Puerto Rico vs. Tokyo, and Tokyo vs. Stockholm. A
pregnant stew has some things going for her. It's easier
and cheaper for her to get to Puerto Rico or Tokyo or
Stockholm and have her abortion there. Travel can be
the biggest item of expense, and we can always get it at
cut rates, if not for free. If you're a straight girl, and
well-liked, your supervisor can be very understanding.
She can give you time off, arrange your schedule so you
can take a working flight to the destination city of
your choice, and have enough layover time. And if
the man involved happens to be a pilot or a flight
engineer, sometimes the airline will go even a bit
further. The supervisor can discreetly arrange to have
the man informed of the situation, even if the pregnant
stew doesn't want to embarrass him. If he doesn't have
the ready cash to contribute to the cost of the abortion, Personnel can arrange to advance the money,
and it can be quietly deducted from future checks in
monthly installments. This saves the dashing pilot
from mortgaging his frozen custard stand or having
to go see his friend at Chase Manhattan. All of it can
be arranged. But first Miss Pregnant Stew has to decide what she wants to do and where she wants to go
to have it done.

This was apparently the purpose of the little group
therapy seminar at Gail's. Since Maryanne had the
least to say of anyone, we all knew she was the little
mother-to-be.

I had been to other meetings of the Society for the
Prevention of Baby Showers. This was Trudy's first.
After the party broke up, we talked it over.

Maryanne was in her second month. The airline was
being very understanding and cooperative. The man
involved was a veteran captain. He had agreed to a
financial settlement. Everything had been arranged.
She had decided to go to Tokyo. The flight was ar-

ranged. She was in Japan for two days. She came home looking great, but still pregnant. She didn't like the Japanese doctor. Now, she was off to Sweden. The purpose of the party was to help her resolve her indecision in advance. Gail didn't want her to go off alone to Stockholm and then come back again in a few days still pregnant.

"Why doesn't Gail go with her?" I suggested.

"Look," said Trudy. "She can't make up the girl's mind for her. If she can't do it here, why should it be easier in Stockholm? If she fiddles around for a few more weeks, it'll be too late. She won't have any choice. No doctor will touch you after four months unless he's a real butcher."

"I didn't know that," I said.

"I didn't know it either. It's what Gail told me."

"Nobody ever wants to admit they're an expert on abortions, do they?"

Anyway, the next time we talked to Gail we asked her if Maryanne was back yet.

"Yes," Gail said. Trudy asked how it worked out.

Gail swore us to secrecy and told us Maryanne had come back from Stockholm, packed all her clothes, got rid of a year's accumulation of assorted junk, and gone back to Sweden to live. "More or less permanently" was the way she put it.

A year passed before we again brought up Maryanne in conversation. Her name came up one night when we were arguing about the best way to keep an international address and phone book. Do you keep names and addresses alphabetically for the whole planet, and carry around a roster the size of a Gideon Bible, or do you have separate little books for each continent?

It was who-do-we-know-in-Sweden night when Trudy said she wondered What Ever Happened to Maryanne? We called Gail and got the last address she had. We put it in the Scandinavian section of our European book, just in case we had time to look her up. We found the time a few months later. I called right after working a flight to Stockholm. Maryanne sounded great. She asked about Gail and all the other kids and we said we'd love to see her except there was so little time and we didn't know the city. But she insisted on seeing us, mostly because she wanted us to see Cynthia. When we found out Cynthia was her baby, we decided to make the effort. She sounded so happy and there are so few happy endings to these kinds of stories.

"Come out for dinner and stay the night," Maryanne said. "It's quite expensive in a taxi but it's only an hour on the train. And you'll get a chance to meet some Swedes. In a hotel the only people you meet are the same people you meet at airports and on planes. Come and bring your pajamas."

She gave us directions and arranged to meet us at the train. It was only a short walk from the station. She looked absolutely gorgeous with no make-up, long hair, as fresh and dewy as a teenager. Home was a rambling old frame house on a crooked street only a few yards from the water, as every neighborhood in the island city of Stockholm seems to be. Lots of children were playing in the yard. A massive fireplace was roaring in the living room. Strange, exotic smells were pouring out of the kitchen. Young girls in their twenties, six of them, popped in and out of the kitchen. We were introduced to them, and they to us. We knew that communal or tribal living was a rampaging world-wide trend, and maybe this was it.

We had a delicious dinner, then the children were packed off to bed including gorgeous little Cynthia, a toddler just beginning to get her walking papers, and we settled down with Maryanne in the living room.

"I often think about the first night I came to this house," she recalled. "I sometimes laugh and say The Lady With The Lamp should be out there in the Baltic Sea, as far as I'm concerned."

"You don't sound bitter," Trudy said.

"I'm not," she said. "I think Cynthia and this place are the greatest things that ever happened to me." And then she told us how she came to Stockholm, as she had gone to Tokyo, determined to have the abortion. She went to the doctor's office. She reacted favorably to his professional bearing and the immaculate conditions of the modern hospital and made the appointment. That afternoon, she took shelter from the rain in a small Konditori, a pastry shop in Stockholm's Old Town, behind the Royal Palace. She still remembered what she ordered that afternoon—an almond pastry and port wine. The place was crowded and she shared a table with a young mother and her son. The woman spoke English and they got to talking and Maryanne admired her youngster. For what seemed like no reason the girl invited her for dinner, at this house.

"I saw what you saw tonight. We sat at two tables for dinner, mothers and children together, and not a man in sight. It was like a family without fathers. All the girls here have children. And none of them are married. They have no husbands. In every case, they didn't want to marry the fathers of their children and they didn't want to have abortions. Two of the girls stay at home, do the housework and care for all the children while the others go out to business and earn money. Sensible, no?"

There was no arguing with that. "The children grow up together. Some of us share bedrooms. One of our girls just left to get married. That's why I could ask you to stay the night."

"Which was the girl who brought you here?" Trudy asked. "We met so many I can't keep their names straight."

"Oh, Helena. She left some weeks ago. She got married, too."

"You have a beautiful child, Maryanne," we told her. "We're so happy for you."

"I'm so lucky to have Cynthia. I have never re-gretted it for a moment. How could I? It is so easy here in Sweden to have an abortion. And so easy *not* to have an abortion. No heat. No sweat. That's what freedom is all about, I think. That's why I say we need a Statue of Liberty out here in the lake some-where saying 'Give me your tired, your confused . . .' "

"Do you ever miss New York, the States, or think about coming back?" we wondered.

"There's no reason to," said Maryanne. "It's a nice place to visit, but I wouldn't want Cynthia to live there." She smiled. We wanted to ask about her par-ents and how they felt about it, but decided that would be prying. We wondered about the father of the baby and how he felt about it, but that would have been prying, too. But Maryanne brought him up without prompting. She told us she was walking with Cynthia through a downtown park when she came face to face with the child's father, airline Captain Walter Renken.

"Dick?" Maryanne said.

"Yeah," he answered. "Wait a minute. I know you. Let me see. Oh yeah, Maryanne. Maryanne Marshall. How you been?"

"Fine. And this is my daughter, Cynthia. Say hello to Captain Renken, Cynthia." The child looked up and smiled.

"Is that . . . ?" Renken asked.

"Yes."

"I heard you were coming here right after you told them you quit. I never understood it, a young girl like you. I still don't."

"It doesn't make any difference what you understand," Maryanne told him. "I'm happy and Cynthia is happy. That's all that counts."

"She's cute. Real cute, Maryanne."

"Yes, she is."

"Is there anything I can do to help out?"

"No. The airline sent me the money they deducted from your check, and I appreciate that. Nothing for you to worry about at all. How's your family?"

"Oh, fine. Great. The oldest boy's in school now. Princeton. I've got another starting next year."

"That sounds wonderful. You must be very proud of them."

"Yeah. I am. Well, I've gotta run. I've got a date with . . . See you soon, OK?"

"OK."

CHAPTER X

"Our Contribution to the Fall of the British Empire"

We love London. Who doesn't? It has all the excitement and ardor of New York without being crude about it. London has regal soul to illuminate its dreary, gray days of drizzle and fog. It's a smashing city and one always high on the monthly bid sheets of every stewardess. We flew New York-London in June, perhaps the nicest month as weather goes. We were so enthralled with the city and its people that we decided to visit there in November, perhaps the worst month as weather goes. The bone-chilling dampness didn't dampen our vacation spirits one bit as we took a cab from the airport to our hotel. Well, it really wasn't a hotel, in the usual sense. It was an apartment building just off Piccadilly Circus, and we were staying there because Alfie Romero, a British purser for the airline, insisted upon it.

"Aye can't understand birds like you," Alfie told us over a beer in a Hong Kong bar. "Here aye am settin' ya up with a really nice flat where it won't cost ya a bloody bob and ya give me an argument. Aye tell ya, I've got good friends in the flat and they're goin' to be gone on a holiday the same time you two will be in London. 'Ere . . . I've even got the key to the flat. Take it and enjoy yourselves."

We flew to London the following night for a four-day vacation. The hack driver, a portly gentleman with bald head, helped us up the steps of the apartment building, tipped his hat and drove away. We lugged our baggage up three flights and opened the door to Flat 3D. It was lovely. The rooms—living, bedroom and bath—were larger than we anticipated from the outside of the building. Graceful pieces of period furniture were tastefully arranged in the living room. Thick, Oriental rugs covered the floor, in some cases one on top of the other. Rich paintings accented the wall areas, and on every table-top and shelf stood tiny but very expensive items—sterling silver chess sets, solid gold cigarette lighters and cases, little jade figurines, and a number of leather-bound books.

"The girl who lives here does pretty well," I commented to Trudy as we moved into the bedroom. I reached for a wall switch and touched a dial. I turned it slowly and the bedroom was bathed in soft, pink light coming from behind the rococo ceiling molding. Another dimmer dial was next to the one I was using; I turned that one and shades of red and magenta glowed from other bulbs hidden behind the molding. The room's dominant feature, a massive bed, took on a passionate meaning in the soft lights, truly fit for a Queen's affair.

"I wouldn't be surprised to see Stanley Kowalski burst through the door any minute," Trudy muttered, pushing on the bed with her hand. "What a passion pit."

"Just don't get sexy with me," I warned, going back into the living room. We eventually unpacked and relaxed with some Scotch we found in the teak liquor cabinet. Alfie had told us to use anything and everything in the flat.

"I'm going to call Sir Willard right now," I said, putting down my drink and going to the phone. It was the one favor we'd promised to do while in London. Sir Willard Hastings Montgomery Wilson was an uncle to Janie Wilson, a fellow stew. He was also one of the ranking members of The House of Commons and, according to Janie, one of the most beloved and powerful men in the British Parliament. She hadn't seen him in six months and asked us to call him and give her best. I dialed the number Janie had given us and, after speaking with three different male secretaries, was connected with Sir Willard.

"I can't tell you how pleased I am that you've called me," Sir Willard said after I introduced myself and passed along Janie's message. He sounded *so* British, so controlled and dignified and positively ramrod. Frankly, I was a little frightened and insecure in his telephone presence.

"Well, it was nice talking with you, sir."

"It was a pleasure speaking with you, too, Miss Jones. And if it would not appear too bold, I'd like to suggest we meet this evening and you allow me to welcome you to London properly. Would that be appropriate?"

"Yes. I mean can you wait a minute?"

"Yes, of course."

I whispered the invitation to Trudy, who was leafing through the *London Times*. She was obviously game, so I accepted.

"Splendid. I'll fetch you at seven-thirty. May I have the name of your hotel?"

"It's not a hotel, sir. It's the apartment of a friend." I gave him the address.

"Splendid. It sounds as though you've found an authentic London bargain, and Lord knows there aren't enough of those these days. I'll have my driver fetch you at seven-thirty."

"Yes, sir."

As the afternoon wore on, we began to feel a definite apprehension about meeting so distinguished a man as Sir Willard. We'd been in the company of U. S. Senators before, but they just didn't inspire the awe of a stately British political leader. My fears became so real that I started answering everything Trudy said with a British accent.

"You sound awful," Trudy told me. "You sound like a real phoney."

"I can't help it, I can't help it. I want to speak correctly and it always come out British. Or Boston."

"Well, that's pretty supid. He wants to hear two American girls, not two yokels with an affected accent. Relax, Rach, he's only another man."

Only another man. Indeed. He happened to be a leader of the British Empire, a world figure, a man of wisdom and culture, a polo player, a man who could enjoy his drinks warm and throw darts and speak the King's English.

"Whatta you know?" I snapped at my roommate.

"That's better, Rach. Now you sound like your old, illiterate self."

There's something about a Rolls Royce. In other cities they can look noveau riche and splashy, but in London they just belong. When we saw this cute beige one pull up in the street below the apartment, we were almost ready. The chauffeur didn't even ring for us. He just stood there, awaiting our pleasure. Princess Margaret and her older sister were never more regal than the two of us riding through Mayfair in that beige chariot. The chauffeur whirled around Carlos Place to let us off directly in front of the entrance to the Hotel Connaught. As he helped us out of the car we practically stumbled into Red Sutherland getting into a very ordinary looking black Rolls. The Connaught looks as though not a thing has changed since King Edward's time. I'd never seen a really old-fashioned, intimate hotel to compare with it for cush and class.

"Sir Willard will meet you in the dining room," the chauffeur said.

The *Sir* gave both of us pause but we didn't bat an eye. It made my blood turn positively blue. In an instant, Sir Willard appeared, telling us we looked smashing and super and escorting us to a huge corner table. As soon as he got the ordering out of the way and the waiter opened the champagne, he began charting the rest of the evening. It turned out to be one of the most marvelous evenings of our lives. Private clubs, gambling, and class, class, class. Everyone, of course, knew Sir Willard. We hated it all to end.

I thought we should say good night in the car, but Sir Willard insisted on seeing us right to the door. I knew I could make the three flights, but I wasn't too confident about him. But he took it as some kind of challenge to his manhood. He even insisted on helping with the vagaries of the double lock on our door. He finally opened it. We thanked him a thousand times. He promised to call us when he came to New York. We promised to alert him on our next trip to London so we could visit the family estate for a long week end. We all kissed goodnight on the cheek and he left. As soon as we latched the door, Trudy peeled off her little black chiffon nothing and put her head under the cold shower. I unzipped my dress and was looking for an Alka Seltzer in the kitchen when I heard the crash. It sounded like a bomb had exploded in the hall. Without thinking, I opened the door and stepped into the hallway. Sir Willard had fallen onto the landing and knelt there clutching his chest.

"What's the matter?" I shouted.

"I'm not sure," he gasped. "This beastly pain . . ."

"Did you fall?" I asked him as I dashed to his side. Trudy came running to the landing wearing nothing but her panties and slip.

"I'll help him into the flat," she suggested. "You're dressed. Go get his chauffeur."

"Yes," said Sir Willard. "Fetch Musgrove. He'll know what to do. The nitroglycerine pills are in a compartment in the car."

Nitroglycerine pills! The poor lamb. He had a heart condition and tonight had been too much for him. I raced downstairs and came back with Musgrove. He seemed very cool about the whole thing. Trudy had helped Sir Willard to the couch. Musgrove thought it would be better if we stretched him out on the big bed. When we turned on the pink lights, the scene was eerie, with Trudy crawling around undressed trying to unfasten his vest and cravat. Musgrove, being very cool, administered the little pills to Sir Willard, telling him to put them under his tongue.

"What about mouth-to-mouth resuscitation?" I asked out loud. Before Musgrove could say anything, Trudy had gone to work. It seemed to help. Musgrove went quietly to the phone to call the doctor.

"We better get dressed before the doctor comes," I suggested to Trudy. We put on long robes and Trudy took a dry towel to her hair. The last hectic ten minutes had sobered me up completely, faster than any Alka Seltzer. Trudy was as calm as a surgical nurse. By the time the doctor arrived, Sir Willard was feeling much better. The doctor suggested he should check into the hospital for a few days for tests. Sir Willard wouldn't hear of it. "The next few days are crucial ones in the House," he said. "I simply can't be absent."

"After the votes this week, I'll go for tests," Sir Willard conceded. "And that's a promise."

The doctor examined him and said it was OK to be moved. They were all full of apologies as they left, and Sir Willard promised to call us when he was feeling better.

We collapsed into what might have been his deathbed, exhausted.

"You know, Rach, if a member of Parliament had died here, it might look pretty strange."

"Yeah," I said. "Poor man, no wonder he tries to live it up . . . like there's no tomorrow."

We spent the next three days in a dizzying whirl with old friends and new. We crowded in some sight-seeing, drooling over the Tower of London jewels, and the Elgin Marbles at the British Museum. We got to the theatre a couple of times, made the rounds of the pubs and discos with another flight crew that landed that afternoon. We took time to send a postcard to Alfie thanking him for arranging for the flat, and before we checked out, we left a very polite note at-tached to a bottle of champagne, thanking our unseen hostess, the flat's tenant.

It was weeks before we managed to catch up with Alfie in New York. He dropped by the stew zoo one night to pick up the set of keys he'd loaned us. We were thanking him for the eleventh time, when he said "Don't mention it, ducks. You sure put that bloody flat on the map now, didn't you?" We didn't know what he meant.

"We did?" Trudy asked innocently, thinking perhaps the jonquils and the Rolls had uplifted the neighbor-hood and caused a little tongue-wagging.

"You mean you didn't see those photos in KINK?" Alfie asked with a chortle. We not only hadn't seen them, we didn't even know what KINK was. It turned out to be one of the most notorious scandal sheets in Europe.

"Samantha sued the bejezuz out of them and they settled for a pretty penny. She never would tell me how much she bloody well got, afraid I'd hit her up for a bloody commission. But I'd say it was plenty." Samantha, it turns out, was the gal in whose flat we had stayed.

"But what could she sue them for, what were her grounds for action?"

"For printing those shots of Trudy in her bed with Sir Willard and making her out a bloody tart."

Trudy looked at me and I looked at her.

Alfie had a real ruptured sense of humor anyway,

and we were positive he was putting us on. But how could he know about Sir Willard? We hadn't told more than seventeen or eighteen thousand people about our adventures with a Member of the British House of Parliament.

"Sir Willard is an old and dear friend and I can't imagine anyone wanting to hurt him in any way," I said with great dignity.

"I don't think it hurt him a bit," Alfie said. "Actually he came out smelling like violets. It's the first family-type scandal that old codger has ever been involved in."

"What do you mean, family-type scandal?" Trudy was screaming. "Where are those photos and why didn't you tell us? If my life has been ruined I think I'm entitled to know what's happening."

Alfie agreed, of course. But he wasn't sure KINK was readily available. It wasn't the kind of thing they keep on file at the British Ministry of Information. We refused to ever speak to him again until he located a copy of that offensive scandal sheet so we could turn it over to our attorneys. After days of suspense he finally showed up with a copy.

It was sort of an anti-climax. Nobody but Alfie and I could possibly recognize Trudy. Nothing showed really except her scanties and her upper lip as she was applying mouth-to-mouth resuscitation. It was the bed, and the passionate early Mae West decor, that made the picture something to cluck over. Trudy wasn't exactly amused at being identified as the swinging Samantha Ashley, but that's hardly grounds for legal action.

Obviously, Musgrove, the chauffeur, took the photos. He was probably going to blackmail Sir Willard.

"What a dreadful thing to do," I said, looking at the magazine again.

"Of course it was bloody dreadful," Alfie said. "But

it was also bloody stupid of the old boy to be running around London with the two of you. I mean, after all, he does have an old lady of his own, you know."

"Yes, we knew that when we went with him," Trudy told Alfie. "Sir Willard told us she was anxious to meet us and that's why he invited us to his country place the next time we're in London."

Alfie looked skeptical. "I'll bet the two of you his old lady raised one big fuss when all this came out. I'll just bet you anything you want."

We didn't bet because we knew we were right and didn't want to take a fellow-employee's money. We received satisfaction enough when we received a lovely note in the mail from Sir Willard's wife personally inviting us to stay with them any time. That note, and the fact we were a part of London's past, was enough to keep us going back to London as often as possible. There is no greater city on earth.

CHAPTER XI

"You Asked For It"

One of the most popular features of our first book was a chapter in which we discussed the celebrities with whom we'd flown. Jack Carter took public offense, Joe Garagiola blessed us on *Today,* Richard Nixon was elected president and the New York Yankees went into a slump.

We wondered when we went to work with this new airline whether we'd have the chance to meet so many public figures again. But we soon discovered that celebrities spend just as much of their time winging across the seas as across the United States. We've had many notables on our international flights, in some cases the same people we got to know on our domestic flights. Pleasantly, we've come to know a whole world of new ones, too.

It might seem to many folks that, after flying and meeting celebrities for so many years, we'd become cynical and jaded. Not so. We're more relaxed in their presence but still feel that small surge of excitement whenever a familiar face walks on the plane and gives us a smile. There's also a tiny surge of feeling when a well-known face walks on the plane and swears at us because his fur-lined baggage was lost on the previous leg of his or her journey. No matter. We take people as they come, for better or for worse, in sickness and in health, lost baggage and all.

Our friends, and a number of readers of our first book, wrote us and encouraged us to include a celebrity list in any sequel we might do. Since this is the sequel to *Coffee Tea or Me?*, we hereby oblige and bend to public demand.

Bob Hope—The last time we flew with him we tried to imitate his gait down the aisle. You know, that famous Hope walk. He didn't seem to notice but we had a ball entertaining the other passengers. He did say goodbye to us at our destination and seemed like a very courteous, warm gentleman on the flight. We're all for that in every passenger.

Big Wilson—How well we remember being interviewed by "Biggie" on WNBC a few years ago. What a doll. What a great big doll. We like his two buddies, too, Vern Ostermeyer and Jim Grau.

Johnny Carson—Good old humble, toe-in-the-sand Johnny. When we flew with him domestically, he told us to stop up sometimes and be on his show. We didn't. Can we come now, oh mighty Carson, and share in the mirth first-hand you give to all those millions of bedded-down viewers? Can we fondle Doc Severinson's Indian fringe and take a discreet whiff of Ed McMahon's breath?

Mayor John Lindsay—He's enough to give you back your faith in politics. What a charmer. We'd happily give him the key to our airplane if he'd give us the key to his city, or the back door of Gracie Mansion.

Dan Rowan and Dick Martin—We wondered if Dick was as big a lover as he's painted to be. We never found out. But they're both nice guys, and you can bet your sweet bippie on that. We told one of their writers a joke once on a flight but they never used it. It was: If Peter Fonda married Jane Fonda . . . you'd have a clear-cut case of incest. And Henry Fonda would have another problem to solve. In retrospect we can see why it wasn't used. But please accept our own fickle finger of fun award for being nice passengers to fly with.

Tom Jones—Some wise-guy stew once told us she heard that Tom Jones wasn't as big a lover as reputed. She told us he had his pants tailored and sewn while he stood in them. Consequently, he never could get his pants off. Now, do you believe that?

Arthur Godfrey—Besides being a nice gentleman, he fills you with confidence. We know that should the cockpit crew all become deathly ill, Mr. Godfrey would simply go up front and land the plane perfectly.

Sonny Tufts—Bless him.

Joan Rivers—A funny, nice lady. It's hard to tell who started making stewardess jokes—Miss Rivers or Shelley Berman. But we're glad one of them did. Joan Rivers can fly with us anytime. The CAB says that, too.

Merv Griffin—He just bubbles on the plane, sits there bubbling and bubbles off the plane. He means it, too.

Gary Moore—Another naturally friendly person. So many people have to try to keep smiling. It just seems to come naturally for Gary.

David Susskind—Such a gentleman and the last of the breed of father who'll whip out his wallet and pictures of his family at the drop of a hot meal tray.

Long John Nebel—Whenever we're at home in New York and at liberty for the evening, we always turn to Long John's talk show on WNBC. Sometimes, especially when Al Lottman is on with John, we really get worked up and start arguing with them. Trudy keeps threatening to go over to the studio some night and punch Lottman in the nose. She wouldn't really do that, of course, but that's how worked up we get. One night we dropped in at the American Airlines' terminal at JFK where John was doing his show for an audience. It was wild; lines of people trying to get into the restaurant at two o'clock in the morning. It was interesting to watch the way Long John gets his guests going in a conversation and then wanders around until it's time to jump back in. Phil Foster, Brooklyn's Ambassador to the world, was there that night at Kennedy. What a scene.

David Frost—David flies frequently between New York and London and I've been tempted to check the passenger manifests ahead of time and work any flight he's on. He's so nice and sincere and attractive. If he ever becomes giddy due to lack of oxygen and proposes, we both accept. He can count on that.

Jimmy Breslin—The king of the late arrivals. More than once we've stood at aircraft doors waiting for Jimmy to come bustling along, hands flying, entourage trailing behind, loose change flying as he grabs newspapers, magazines and whatever else on the run. A few minutes later, bolstered by a fast two drinks, he settles down and delights everyone as a passenger.

Mike Douglas—Ever since he got over his fear of flying, Mr. Douglas has relaxed while flying. He's a lovely guy, and it's nice now not to find fingernails embedded in the armrests.

Dustin Hoffman—He graduates at the head of the passenger class everytime.

Dick Cavett—What a doll he is, despite what the ratings say.

Virginia Graham—I had a lovely time being on her show and have had the chance to serve her on flights. She's a wonderful lady with capacity for pleasant filibuster.

Bob Newhart—If he was as funny in the accounting office as he is on TV and flights, we'd hate to see the books he audited.

Chet Huntley—We're certainly going to miss Mr. Huntley on TV. He's always been our favorite newscaster and one of our favorite passengers.

Veronica Lake—Miss unpretentious of all time. She's the most natural big name we've ever flown with. She was on her way to London to promote her autobiography, *Veronica,* and she gave us autographed copies. What a book!

Jack Douglas—He's weird. We asked what he'd like to eat and he mumbled something like, "Shut up and eat your seatbelt." Very weird.

Don Knotts—All the stews have a bet going that beneath his seemingly meek and mild exterior lurks a tiger on the loose, a raging male animal clawing its way through the women of the world. You can't prove it by us but if anyone has any information concerning this theory, please write our publisher.

Joe Garagiola—He was upset when he interviewed us on *Today* because we'd categorized baseball players as cheap dates in our first book. He even brought it up again as we were leaving the studio and were paying him fifteen cents each for the coffee they served us.

Other good-guy celebrity travelers are:

Rocky Graziano	Irv Kupcinet
Louis Nye	Leonard Lyons
Dean Martin	Bob Considine
Tony Randall	William Holden
Liz Trotta	Jackie Robinson
John Wayne	David Brinkley
Bill Cullen	Shelley Berman
Joe Richer	Carl Reiner
Gig Young	Sen. Eugene McCarthy
Woody Allen	Sam Levenson
Henry Fonda	Pearl Bailey
Arthur Treacher	Tiny Tim
Brad Crandall	Morey Amsterdam
Steve Allen	William B. Williams
R. H. Sutherland	John Forsythe
Soupy Sales	Cassius Clay
Andy Williams	Charlton Heston
Jayne Meadows	Jack Pearl

Wendie Regalia
Nicholas Johnson
Phyllis Diller
Raymond Burr
Louis Armstrong
Glen Campbell
Sarah Vaughn
Joe O'Brien
Barry Farber
Dan O'Shea
Joe Namath
Peggy Cass
Walter Cronkite
Goldie Hawn
John Gambling
Bill Cosby
Jackie Gleason
Jackie Douglas
Sid Caesar
Tony Martin
Hugh Downs
Pierre Berton
Philip Roth
Billy Taylor

Gregory Peck
Ed Joyce
Jonathan Winters
Harry Belafonte
Robert Vaughn
Sterling Hayden
Bill Mazer
Rodney Dangerfield
George C. Scott
Phil Donahue
Lee Phillips
Jim Gerard
Martha Deane
Tony DeHaro
F. Lee Bailey
Orson Bean
Fred Feldman
Suzzette McKiernan
Fred Robbins
Ralph Nader
Carol Burnett
Sugar Ray Robinson
Duke Ellington
Bob Barker

The following celebrities have also flown with us:

Jack Carter
Jerry Lewis
George Jessel
Danny Kaye
Sal Mineo
Buddy Rich
Rex Reed
Robert Goulet
Gary Morton
Barbra Streisand

Elizabeth Taylor
Jack Paar
Mike Nichols
Bette Davis
Johnny Mathis
Jack Palance
Art Linkletter
The Management of the
    New York Telephone
    Company

CHAPTER XII

"I Promise"

I walked up the aisle of the 707 and casually observed each passenger. Most were asleep. Dinner had been served and cleared, most cabin lights were off and the aircraft took on that peaceful, mysterious quality of night flight. We were surprised at the heavy load of passengers. Usually, the late departure from Miami for Buenos Aires was light. This night, the plane was full, mostly with businessmen but with an appropriate mix of women and children. We'd worked hard getting dinner served and cleared. Now, with the night ahead of us and a sleepy group of passengers, we could relax.

I smiled at one sleeping passenger, a Mister Juarez. I remembered him when he boarded. Juarez was a young man. I figured him for a student. He was dressed like one—chino pants, sweater and loafers. He seemed shy and unsure, the way he responded to my greeting during the boarding process. He just nodded and looked away.

Now Mr. Juarez was curled up in his seat, his head burrowed into the pillow and his youthful long legs twisted in search of room. He looked cute like that. That's why I smiled. I moved up the aisle but turned to see Mr. Juarez open his eyes and look at me. The eyes were black and wide awake. The cuteness was gone. It was a little disconcerting.

I went back to the galley and contemplated how to pass the time. A card game could always be started, either with another stew or one of the still awake businessmen. I could always continue reading a book, but

the one I was reading had bogged down in the middle
and I'd lost interest. I decided to do nothing, at least
for the moment. Outside, through the tiny round window in the galley exit door, the night was total. A solid
cloud cover had formed a huge blanket ten-thousand
feet below; if you jumped, would you bounce on the
blanket or just fall through? I often wondered about
things like that, always knowing the answer but finding
the unreasonable alternatives interesting. Night flight
usually served my thoughts. Lately, those thoughts
ended up on Bill, a new boyfriend. Our relationship
had gone further than I'd anticipated, or even desired.
Lately, I found more and more disenchantment with
young men. Too often, they failed to provide the one
single human ingredient I held most important. Truth!
Complete truth and honesty. Acceptance of what one
is, and without any attempts to seem otherwise. Bill
had showed promise in this regard, at least in the early
months of our dating. But he, too, eventually drifted
into tall tales, tales calculated to boost his worth in
my eyes. Instead of enjoying his true situation, that of
a bright young man with ambition and a future, he
became the young man who had already made it. It
wasn't true. He hadn't made it, and there wasn't a
whole corps of people after his talents. That would
come. But he wanted me to believe he was already
there. And this is what bothered me.

Even simple promises were broken. I recalled a
recent evening when Bill broke a date with me.

"Rach," he'd said on the phone. "I'm up to here
with work. I'm just going to have to stay at the office
and grind it out. Please understand."

"I understand, Bill. Please don't feel badly. Get
your work done and we'll make it tomorrow night."

"Great. I love you."

"That's nice to hear. Work hard."

Just like married people, I thought. But I found

out through a friend of his that he didn't work that night. He'd gone to his apartment and watched a football game. Just Bill and some beer. He wanted to watch the game without me or anyone around. He just wanted to be alone. So why didn't he say just that? Why didn't he say he just wasn't in the mood for the movie we were going to see? Just be honest, Bill. You're entitled.

I picked up my book and began reading, hoping to break through the logjam of detail and move on to more of the story. Just as it seemed I'd reached that point in the book, the galley curtain opened and Mr. Juarez stood there.

"Oh, hi, Mr. Juarez. Short nap?" I closed my book and smiled. Mr. Juarez said nothing. He reached into his belt and withdrew a long, thin knife. He pointed it at me.

My reaction was to swallow hard and lose my smile. I knew it was another hijacking. What number would that make it for the year? Sixty? Or was it up to seventy? Still, despite my immediate knowledge of the situation, I was forced to ask, "Why the knife, Mr. Juarez? What do you want?"

"Havana." He said it flatly.

"I see."

"Tell your captain." His black eyes were without expression.

"What do you want me to tell him, Mr. Juarez?"

"Tell him to turn to Cuba."

"I think *you* should tell him, Mr. Juarez."

"I will tell him. We will walk there together. I will walk behind you. The knife will always be there."

I nodded and sighed. His accent was Spanish, although not very pronounced. He probably had spent considerable time in the United States. I couldn't decide which Spanish-speaking country was home for Juarez. I'd ask.

"Where is your home, Mr. Juarez?"

"Guatemala," he said too quickly. His face hardened. "No more questions, Miss. We will go to your captain."

"Yes, I told you I would take you. But you might at least tell me why you want to go to Cuba. I'd be interested in knowing that. It won't make any difference because you will go. No one in the crew is going to fight you. I'm sure you know that from all the past hijackings."

Juarez allowed his eyes to stray from me for the first time. He glanced at the floor and then to the small round window in the door. He could see his face reflected in the glass, just the center portion, the eyes, nose and mouth. He looked back at me. "Please don't try anything, Miss. I will kill you. I promise that."

"I know you will, Mr. Juarez. I suppose you have good reason to want to kill and go to Cuba. I hope you have, anyway."

"I have."

"Good."

"I will not wait any longer, Miss."

"All right. Let's go."

Before I could step past Juarez and lead him to the cockpit, another stewardess, Connie Cowles, stepped into the galley. Mr. Juarez held the knife along his hip and glared at me. Connie said hello to him and went directly to the galley refrigerator. She opened it and brought out a can of Coke. "Thirsty passenger," she said, smiling at Juarez.

Connie left the galley with the Coke, saying over her shoulder, "How about some cards, Rach? We've got a live wire in the back."

"Maybe later, Connie."

Juarez visibly relaxed. I hadn't noticed his body tense when Connie appeared. But now his shoulders sagged, and he leaned against a serving counter, the knife still at his right side.

"Shall we go to the captain, now, Mr. Juarez?"

"Yes." He didn't move to allow me past him. He just leaned there and looked at his face in the window.

"You know, Mr. Juarez, no one is going to try to stop you on this plane. It's the airline policy. The safety of the passengers comes first. No one will stop you, except in Cuba."

"What do you mean?" Juarez's eyes snapped to attention.

"You've heard of the new policy there, haven't you?" I asked, showing no emotion.

"You mean of returning those who steal airplanes to the country of the plane?"

"Yes."

"It applies only to those who steal a plane for fun, Miss. Not for those who go to Cuba to escape the lies of America. Political refugees are welcome by Fidel."

"Are you a political refugee, Mr. Juarez?"

"I am a man who has been lied to. That is why I go."

"Who lied to you?" I was finding it more difficult to contain my emotions. I wanted to reach out and touch the man in the galley, reach out with my voice and persuade him to reconsider. But I was afraid of showing any enthusiasm, any zeal, for the conversation.

"Everyone lies, Miss. Everyone."

"I don't lie, Mr. Juarez."

The young man smiled. His teeth were fully exposed and his eyes shone. He reached and took one of the airline sample cigarette packs, extracted a cigarette and lighted it.

"Miss, I think you would like to make me talk about myself and forget what I am about to do. Others have done that. In college, my advisor always wanted

to have me think differently. He always talked to me
and asked me questions and tried to have me change
my opinions of America."

I reached for a cigarette. I didn't smoke, but I
needed something to break the tension. I placed the
cigarette in my mouth and looked at Juarez. He
lighted it. Neither of us said anything for a minute.
The light came on, indicating the cockpit crew wanted
something, probably a stewardess to remove the dinner
trays.

"The captain wants me," I said, nodding to the
light. "They want their dinner trays cleaned up. Can
I go and come back without you? I promise not to
say anything or do anything. Will you believe me?"

"No. Since the captain wants you, it is the best
time for you to take me."

"Please, Mr. Juarez. I'd like to prove to you that
everyone doesn't lie. Please?"

Juarez found my request ludicrous. The lies to
which he was referring were big lies, so big that he
wondered if any human being could help but make
them. He had been promised a life of plenty in the
United States, but all he could see ahead was prejudice
against his origins. He saw the Puerto Ricans, brothers,
living in poverty and without hope. He saw war being
waged against brothers in Asia. He watched empty
dreams and pompous political promises for South
America. His professors at college lied to him, according to what he held up as truth. Juarez looked
at me and glared.

"Please, Mr. Juarez. Let me go by myself. Then, if
you still want to hijack the flight to Cuba, I'll take
you up front. I promise."

My request was ludicrous. But Juarez granted it.

"How long will you be, Miss?"

"Two minutes."

"No more."

"No more."

I went to the flight deck and took the trays away. The cockpit crew started to joke with me but I didn't participate. The flight engineer muttered, "Stuck-up broad," as I left.

"See?" I said to Juarez as I put the trays on the counter.

"Where are we now?" he asked.

"I'm not sure." I checked my watch. "About over Bogota."

Juarez tried to sense any change in the plane's direction. There was none.

"A stewardess lied to me once," Juarez said.

"Really? When?"

"Recently. A month ago."

A girl had lied. She had said she loved him, but she had gone off with a rich American boy with a big car and good clothes and money to entertain her. But she had been more than a girl, she had been a stewardess.

"And I am a stewardess. Do you want to hurt me for that, Mr. Juarez?"

"Yes. No, no. But she was no different. You are no different."

I took another cigarette. "Do you believe Fidel Castro won't lie to you?" I asked, accepting another light from the young man.

"I don't know."

"He might. What will you do then?"

Juarez rubbed his eyes and didn't answer. He thought of our position in the sky and knew every minute took us further away from Cuba. He had to act. No more wasted time talking with me, this stewardess. He gripped the knife tighter and involuntarily jabbed it at me. I suppressed a scream and did nothing. My voice was tight as I asked, "Where did you get the money to buy your ticket?"

"From the university. From the student loan office. It was to be tuition money."

"It was good of them to lend it to you."

"Yes."

"And you lied to *them.*" Juarez looked puzzled. "You told them you would use the money to go to school. Instead, you bought an airplane ticket."

Juarez grinned. "Yes. It is only fair that I lie."

"I'd never lie to you, Mr. Juarez."

"Why not?"

"Because I like you."

"*She* said that."

"The stewardess?"

"Yes."

"I'm sorry. She shouldn't have lied."

Juarez swallowed against tears that were beginning to form. "I loved her. I told her that."

"And you weren't lying, were you, Mr. Juarez."

"No. Not about that."

Connie Cowles came back in again. "Come on, Rach, it's a good game. He's a nice guy."

"In a few minutes." Connie looked at Mr. Juarez. The knife was hidden at his side, and he smiled at her. Connie looked at me and winked. It was a familiar sight to see a stewardess standing in the galley with a young male passenger after others had gone to sleep. It was an ideal time to make a pitch for the stew. A number of them had been made at Connie in the same manner. Obviously, she thought I liked this one. Good for me.

Connie Cowles left the galley.

"Mr. Juarez?" I asked.

"What?"

"You don't really want to do this, do you?"

"Yes, I do. I can see nothing else."

"But you could have done it so much more simply. You could have gone to Cuba from Mexico City. You didn't have to hijack a plane and hold a knife on me."

Juarez rubbed his eyes and stretched his neck. "I'm very tired," he said.

"You wanted to frighten me, didn't you? To make me know what the other stewardess had done to you?"

"I don't wish to harm you."

"But you are harming me. And you're harming everyone on the plane. But most of all, you're harming yourself."

"Perhaps that is true. But it is too late, isn't it? I must go to Cuba now. If I do not, you will have me arrested in Buenos Aires."

I put my hand to my mouth and tried not to say what I was going to say. I didn't want to make a promise and not keep it. I didn't want to contribute another lie to Mr. Juarez's life.

"I won't tell anyone, Mr. Juarez. I promise I won't. If you'll go back to your seat, we'll have dinner when we get to Buenos Aires. You can find a job there and earn enough to fly back to America and pay the university. Please, Mr. Juarez, believe me and do this for yourself." The cockpit light flashed again in the galley. Juarez saw it. So did I.

"They want you again, Miss."

"Yes, I know."

The knife felt heavy in Juarez's hand. He took a deep breath and let it hang loosely at his side. He left the galley and went back to his seat. The moment he was out of my sight, I shuddered and sobbed. But I managed to compose myself before Connie Cowles appeared to fetch coffee for the card-playing passenger.

"Hey, the boys up front want something," she said, noting the light.

"Go see what they want, will you, Connie? I'm sick of the corny jokes."

"Sure."

Mr. Juarez sat passively for the rest of the flight.

He declined breakfast with a shake of his head, never taking his eyes from the window next to him. As the passengers filed from the plane at Buenos Aires, Juarez looked directly at me as I stood by the door. In daylight, he appeared even younger than in the glow of the galley. Large circles under his eyes dominated a handsome face. And his eyes were filled with fear.

"Wait for me in the lobby," I said quickly. "I'll be there in ten minutes." I watched him walk down the exit ramp. Two uniformed police stood at the entrance to the building. Juarez walked past them, his hand in his jacket pocket where I knew the knife was kept.

The crew hurried through operations and walked together towards the lobby and the waiting limousine.

"I'm not going with you," I told Connie. Connie didn't have to ask why. She saw Mr. Juarez standing in a corner. I split off from the party and walked towards him. He was nervous; his eyes flashed around in search of a uniform.

"We can eat here in the airport," I said. Juarez nodded and followed me to the airport restaurant. We ate, and I paid the cashier. Outside in the lobby, I extended my hand. Juarez almost took it. Instead, his face turned cold and his hand went to his jacket pocket.

"Goodbye, Mr. Juarez. I've enjoyed meeting you." I walked away.

Later that month, as I sat watching the late news with Trudy, the newscaster reported another hijacking of an American aircraft to Cuba. It had been diverted during a flight from Buenos Aires to Miami.

"Damn nuts," Trudy said. "They ought to lock them all up for life."

I nodded sleepily and turned off the set.

CHAPTER XIII

"We Don't Want
to Overthrow Anybody"

We didn't know Sandra Ruse was an Arab. Her name didn't reflect it nor did her blonde hair and blue eyes. But her father was Egyptian, and her brother lived and worked in Cairo as a civil engineer.

Sandra's mother was divorced from her father and lived in Tel Aviv. So did Sandra's boyfriend. Naturally, Sandra bid often for the New York-Tel Aviv run. She was senior enough to receive it often, and worked it as many as six months out of the year.

It was our first month on the Tel Aviv run, so Sandra became our guide and protector during layovers there. We stayed at The Dan, an old luxury hotel in the middle of town. One day, we'd been out sightseeing since early morning and were entering the hotel when the commotion started. Two Israeli policemen had a fat man in a combination headlock and armlock in the corner of the lobby. An hysterical American woman stood jabbering at the police while the hotel manager tried to calm everybody down. We joined the rest of the crowd and went over to the scene.

"We've got him," one of the policeman was saying to the manager. "The cat burglar. It's him."

It was comical. How could anyone call the fat man beneath the policemen's bodies a cat burglar? An elephant burglar, maybe. But not a cat burglar.

"I was coming out of the shower," the American lady was yelling, "and there he was. This . . . this . . . this cat burglar. He was taking my watch from the dresser. I screamed and he tried to talk me into being quiet but I screamed anyway. I was hoping one of the other ladies on the tour would hear and come to my aid. Oh, it was awful."

"Did he attempt to molest you, madam?" one of the police asked. The other officer was sitting in an overstuffed chair with the cat burglar sitting on top of him. The policeman had his arm around the fat man's throat. The alleged burglar sputtered and stammered and gasped for breath.

"Molest me? Absolutely not!" The American woman seemed both offended and slightly flattered that anyone might molest her. The captive winced and shook his head violently. Obviously, molesting this American club lady was not his intention.

The officer being slowly pressed to death in the chair relaxed his grip on his captive. The fat fellow pulled away and fell to his knees before the American matron.

"Please, lovely lady," he pleaded, rolling his eyes and making his belly shake. "You have so much while I am poor. My children suffer because I am sick and cannot work. See?" He pulled a picture from his pocket in which a fat woman and eleven children were lined up. "My heart is bad and my wife must harvest the modest field behind our hovel. God will forgive me, fair lady. Will you? Will you spare my family from the consequences of my foolish indiscretions?"

"Oh, all right," she responded, fluffing her dyed hair in the wall mirror. "But if you natives in underdeveloped countries would stop having babies and learn something from us about birth control, maybe you could pull yourselves up."

"Yes, yes, gracious lady. Your wisdom is great." The whole thing struck us as ludicrous. One look at his wife in the photograph and you knew they'd probably practiced birth control for years—natural birth control by two people who didn't want to be close to each other. Besides, Israel is hardly an underdeveloped nation with an overpopulation problem. Oh well, he was a thief and played any game he had to play to avoid being sent to jail. He was sort of likable in a grotesque way, sort of the lovable bumbler.

"You will not press charges?" the officer asked, disappointed in not being able to run the thief in to his superior.

"No," the woman answered. "We Americans realize justice must take strange forms in the lesser developed areas of the world. This man is poor. I think he's learned his lesson."

"Oh, yes, benevolent lady," the thief chanted.

"Here. Take this." She handed him ten dollars.

"Bless you, bless you," he murmured, backing away from the crowd and winking at the policeman.

When Sandra's boyfriend took us to lunch, we told him about the scene in the lobby. It was as amusing to him as it was to us. He explained that the so-called cat burglar was a sad-sack named Wagid Schlamiel. His claim to fame was that he was the only second-story man in Tel Aviv, a city with almost a total absence of crime. Wagid had been arrested many times but seldom was sent to jail. He was a master at playing on the sympathy of his victims, usually turning their anger into pity for him. Nine of the eleven children in his readily available photograph belonged to neighbors. Another thing he had going for him was that his needs were small. He was content with a modest income, just enough to sustain himself and his family and to avoid taking a steady job. Consequently, he never risked any big jobs. It was more his style to hang around, sometimes in janitor's clothing, sometimes in bellhop costume, and wait for someone to leave their hotel room door open. In and out. Maybe a ring, or some souvenirs which he'd sell back to the original merchant at half price. Sometimes he even found some loose cash lying about. One of the big advantages in operating small was that the tourists often didn't miss anything until they returned home. Or the amounts were so small, Wagid could easily pay back any thefts. According to Sandra's beau, the famed Tel Aviv cat burglar had never worked The Dan before. He usually confined his activity to the luxury hotels along Herzliya, Tel Aviv's Riviera. Sandra's boyfriend chuckled at the fact Wagid had come downtown.

"He's really a pleasant institution here in Tel Aviv," he told us as we finished lunch. "Actually one of the tourist attractions, along with the war."

Sandra went off with her boyfriend as Trudy and I went to our room for a nap. We'd just dozed off when a heavy knocking on the door jarred us awake. It was Sandra.

"My room," she gasped. "It's been robbed."

We threw on robes and went with her down the hall. She showed us where she'd left some costume jewelry that morning. There were also a few loose bills missing. But most important was a large, brown envelope. According to Sandra, it contained drawings of a new, low-cost housing development outside of Cairo. Her brother was involved in the planning of the community and had sent Sandra's mother a set of the plans. He was proud of what he was doing and wanted to share it with his family. The envelope was missing.

"Why would any thief want plans like that?" I asked Sandra.

"He probably just took the envelope and didn't know what was in it," Trudy offered. "Maybe he'll drop it in the mail when he finds out."

Sandra agreed with Trudy's analysis. We all went

down to the desk, after stopping off at our room so we could dress, and reported the theft to the desk manager. He was very upset and promised to have the police there within the hour. As we were walking away from him, he yelled after us.

"Did the priest find you?" he asked.

"What priest?" Sandra asked.

"The monk. The Catholic monk. He came to the desk before and asked for you."

We listened as the desk manager told the story. This man in a long, brown robe came to the desk and asked for the name of the American girl in Room 12G, Sandra's room. He explained to the desk manager that he'd been summoned to hear the girl's confession but had forgotten her name. The manager gave Sandra's name to him.

"What else can you tell us about him?" I asked.

"Well, he was fat . . . and he kept burping, if you'll pardon the expression. He kept his hand up to his face all the time, either by his mouth when he . . . burped . . . or to play with his beard."

"Was he carrying anything?" Sandra asked.

The desk manager thought a moment. "Why yes. He was carrying a large brown envelope."

Sandra's brother's plans. But why did he want to know her name? The answer to that was known two hours later when three members of Israel's counter-intelligence agency came to the hotel and arrested us for conspiring to overthrow the government of Israel. We were taken to their headquarters where the chief of operations, a muscular man with a black patch over one ear, sat across the desk. In a corner slumped Wagid Schlamiel, still dressed in his brown priest's robe but with his phony beard laying on a table next to him. He avoided our eyes when we entered and picked at his thumb.

The three of us started yelling at once to protest

our arrest and the chief allowed us to yell all we wanted. Finally, after we ran out of words, he turned to Wagid and said, "Now, suppose you tell us your story, Mr. Schlamiel. Again, for the sake of these girls."

Wagid squirmed in his chair. He started talking to the wall but the chief told him to turn around and face us. He did so with much agony.

"He's a thief," I blurted out. "The cat burglar."

Wagid jumped up and clutched his breast. He looked at the intelligence chief with watery eyes and moaned, "Once, Wagid was a thief. But Wagid is first a Jew, and then a thief. No, no, Wagid is not even a thief any longer. Now, I am a patriot. A patriot of Israel." He sort of sang the last words like a battle hymn.

"Go on," the chief said. "And stop this terrible act. Just tell the story as it happened."

Wagid paced the room, his brown robe flowing behind him. He told us how he had suspected Sandra from the moment he laid eyes on her in the hotel.

"Suspected me of what?" she demanded.

"Of being a spy for their side," Wagid answered.

Sandra started yelling again but the chief told her to stop.

Wagid continued with his story. He claimed that he slipped into Sandra's room in search of evidence of her espionage activity. And he found it in the brown envelope. Wagid pointed to it on the chief's desk.

"That envelope is mine," Sandra said. "It's mine and contains plans my brother drew up in Cairo."

There was stunned silence in the room.

"So you admit these plans are from Cairo," the chief said.

"Yes. But they're not plans for anything important. Just a community of low-cost housing that my brother drew up."

"With walkways on the walls surrounding it, Miss Ruse?" the chief asked suspiciously. "And with gun turrets at each corner?"

Sandra jumped up and grabbed the plans from the chief's hands. "Where? What gun turrets and walkways?"

"There, Miss Ruse." We all got up and looked. Sure enough, small, broken lines outlined turrets and walkways.

"But this is all nonsense," I said. "We're just airline stewardesses, not spies. Sandra is engaged to a young man in Tel Aviv. And if she says these plans from her brother are of a low-cost housing development, then that's what they are."

"I'm sorry, but I can only go by what facts I have before me. These are difficult and dangerous times in Israel. We have discovered the most innocent people to be involved in espionage activity for the Arab side. And you will admit, I'm sure, that airline stewardesses have been known in the past to smuggle various materials for a fee. Is that not true?"

"Well, sure it's true," Trudy said. "We've known girls who got involved in smuggling. But not *us!*"

The chief ignored Trudy and continued. "We must also consider the fact that Miss Ruse is an Arab. And her brother lives on the other side. No, I am sorry but I can do nothing but detain you here until a further investigation can be made."

Sandra was boiling. She banged her fist on the desk and turned hateful eyes on Wagid Schlamiel.

"You're a cheap, two-bit thief, you damn fat elephant. You broke into my room wearing that ridiculous monk's costume and stole the envelope and my jewelry and my cash. Give it back!"

Wagid looked at the chief and shrugged his shoulders.

"Give the cash and jewelry back," the chief said to Wagid.

He reached beneath his robe and pulled out Sandra's things.

"See," she shrieked. "He's just a thief. You can't believe him."

"Unfortunately, Miss Ruse, service to a nation can be performed by many different kinds of people. Yes, this man is a thief. But in this case he has performed important services for Israel. I cannot overlook that."

"And what about us?" I demanded. "They're not *our* plans. Why are we being detained?"

"Because it is necessary." He got up and gestured towards the door. We went to it and were escorted by three young and handsome Israeli agents to our cells, which really were rooms without windows at the rear of the building.

We spent the next hour yelling to each other through the walls. It took us the hour to realize that the right should be granted us to contact the American Embassy. Then we all yelled in unison for a guard. But instead, our screaming brought the chief himself. He calmly opened the doors and indicated we were to precede him up the hall to his office. He was as charming and polite as he was when he had arrested us, only this time he was letting us go.

"Why?" Trudy asked. I wished she hadn't; it might start him reconsidering.

"Because I have checked with certain sources in Cairo and they assure me the plans are of a low-cost housing development. Even the Arabs have compassion for their poor."

"But what about the gun turrets and walkways?" I asked.

"A simple contingency in time of stress. In the United States you plan such developments with perhaps a lake or playground. Here, in the Near East, we plan with barbed wire and walls. Unfortunate, but someday that will change."

He thanked us for our patience and apologized for

our detention. We were leaving his office when Sandra asked, "What about my brother? He's not a spy?"

"No, Miss Ruse, of course not. He's simply a hardworking and dedicated civil engineer in Cairo. I checked him with my source, too."

"When you say source, you mean an Israeli spy, I assume." That was Trudy again, prolonging things.

"No, not an Israeli spy, Miss Baker. I check these things with the Egyptian head of counter-intelligence. We attended the university together in London. He wouldn't lie to me nor would I deceive him. Convenient, yes?"

"Convenient and confusing," I muttered, grabbing Trudy by the arm and making sure she didn't ask any more questions. Sandra did manage to ask for the plans back, but was refused.

"Even though it is a housing development, Miss Ruse, it is helpful for us to have such plans. Since they were only for your personal use, it should not matter, should it? And if your brother ever wishes to leave Cairo and come to Israel, please assure him he is welcome. He's a fine engineer."

I'd never felt so free before as we left the building and breathed in the night air of Tel Aviv. Sandra's boyfriend was waiting for us with a car and drove us back to The Dan. We thanked him, declined his offer of a drink, and happily settled into our room. I was first into the shower and was happily soaping when I heard the heavy thumping on the door. Trudy answered it and let out an audible yelp.

"What's the matter?" I yelled over the sound of the water.

"It's him," she yelled in response.

"Who?"

"Schlamiel."

"Don't let him in."

"He's in."

I threw on my robe and came out of the bathroom. Schlamiel was half in and half out of the room, Trudy having pinned his torso against the door frame with the door.

"Mercy, mercy, sweet lady," he was intoning, his eyes rolling towards the heavens.

"Get away from us," I commanded, helping Trudy push on the door.

"Only one moment of your time precious young things," he said. "In the name of my wife and eleven children. In the name of Allah."

"Oh, let him in, Trudy," I said disgustedly. "If he makes a move I'll smash his fat head in with this." I picked up a lamp and held it ready to strike. He eyed it nervously as Trudy eased the pressure on the door and allowed him to breath again.

"A thousand thank-yous," Wagid said, fishing into the pocket of his blue coveralls. He handed Trudy a bunch of paper money.

"What's that for?" I asked.

"It is one half of what Wagid received from the chief. You see, Wagid was paid as an informer. But since his actions have caused you grief, he wishes to give to you half of the money."

Trudy handed me the money—100 pounds, about thirty-three dollars in American currency. I looked at my partner and she was absolutely melting on the spot. I expected any minute to see her fling herself into Wagid's arms and mother him to death. But I injected some hard-nosed reality into the scene.

"Why only one hundred pounds, Schlamiel? Didn't he pay you four hundred?" It was a guess, but Wagid didn't know that. He licked his lips and fished into his pocket again.

"Of course. I forget. Here." He handed me another hundred pounds.

"That's better."

"A thousand pardons. It is just that Wagid is poor and has many children." He fished out his photograph of the neighborhood brood and told us all about his wife tilling their modest field, etc., etc., etc.

"We've heard all that before, Schlamiel," I said, surprised at how tough I could sound. "Thanks for the split, friend. Now on your way." Bogart. Or at least a distaff Cagney.

"Of course, of course. You are too kind to even allow me to enter your room." I turned on my heel and went back to the shower. I no sooner stepped under the spray when I heard Trudy scream, "Rachel. Come quick." I flew out of the tub, tossed the robe on and ran into the bedroom. There was Trudy trying to wrest her pocketbook from Wagid. I made right for the lamp and Wagid made right for the door, leaving the purse in Trudy's hands.

"Forgive me, forgive me," he moaned all the way down the hall.

"Call the desk," I said.

"Let's not, Rach," Trudy said. "He's so poor and he has all those kids. I think people like us from fortunate nations should have pity on underdeveloped nations. Take birth control, for instance. It seems to me that . . ."

CHAPTER XIV

"Camera Means Bedroom in Italian"

I couldn't keep my head back any longer, although Trudy seemed perfectly comfortable. "It's incredible," she kept saying. I looked up again. Yes, it was incredible—and beautiful.

"How many years did the guide book say Michelangelo laid on his back to paint those frescos?" Trudy asked.

"Four." We both turned to see who'd answered Trudy's question. He was a young, handsome priest.

"Thank you," Trudy said.

Trudy was smiling at him, very cool and very institutional. I ran my wet finger through the guidebook while I took another look at him. He was terribly young and not too dark. The black of his cassock seemed to accent the reddish glints in his hair. He had a bellringing ultra-bright smile and absolutely devastating indentations in his gaunt olive cheeks. He was much too young to be a full-blooded anointed priest. There are so many varieties of priests in Rome, one takes them as part of the scenery unless they happen to zip by, cassocks flying, on a Vespa motorbike. Then you smile at the quaintness of it all. I tried to smile and I managed to nod.

"You are most welcome," the padre said. I felt he was talking to me, but I could see he was concentrating on Trudy.

"Is this your first visit at Vatican City?" he asked Trudy. His English was good. But I noticed that he didn't quite seem to be able to get the right accent on the right syllable. The effect, like Rozzano Brazzi and Marcello Mastroianni, was even more devastating. You felt he was reading off some invisible cue card. His eyes were saying all the important things.

"Yes, it is," I said.

"Ah, it is never as wonderful as it is that very first time," he said.

"But we envy you being able to come here often, don't we?" Trudy was saying to me.

I nodded.

"I do not come so often," he said sadly. "The *turistas* are here very many times in great numbers. Some visions are more nearly enjoyable when you can be without anybody else."

We told him we agreed.

"Are you Americana or English ladies?" he asked.

Nobody from England talks like girls from Louis-ville. I was positive he knew that. But, on the other hand, I couldn't tell Southern Italian from Northern Italian so maybe our accents *didn't* stand out. Trudy said we were Americans. "We are airline stew-ardesses," she explained.

"Oh, yes, hairline styling is a very good business in Rome, too." Trudy broke up and tried again. I went into my little pantomime number. With arms extended I made like a Boeing 747. Trudy looked in her dic-tionary and she couldn't find the word for steward.

"Alitalia," I said very cleverly.

"Ah, yes," he said. "You work for an American hairline." We weren't going to quibble. His English was still many kilometers ahead of our Italian. "Your hairline is very charitable in allowing you liberties."

"No, they're not," we said in chorus. "We're taking a few days' vacation in Rome."

"It is still very charitable if they allow," he insisted.

"It was my idea," I explained. "We've flown *tons* of people to Rome and yet all we know about the Vatican is from seeing the movie."

"We understand," he smiled. "We are very pleased. We are sure the Eternal City will please you. What can we do to help make your first visit something of exciting memory?"

"Do you live here?" Trudy asked.

"My work is here," he said. "My *camera* is just a few steps out of the city."

"Are you a photographer?" I heard myself asking.

"No," he said, staring at the tiny Instamatic Trudy had slung over her shoulder.

"What kind of camera do you have?" Trudy asked him.

"Just big enough for a bed," he smiled. "Very tiny. But what more do we need?" I looked at Trudy and she looked at me. Trudy felt we weren't getting through to him. I wasn't at all sure. She went diving into the dictionary again and came up acting like a Girl Scout. "Camera means bedroom in Italian," she hissed at me under her breath.

"I'm glad you asked before we knew," I said. "Now I wouldn't have the nerve any more."

"Are you Catholic?" he asked us.

"Oh, no," I volunteered. I didn't know whether that was the right thing to say or not. The fact that it was true seemed slightly irrelevant. Trudy shook her head in a way that seemed very apologetic to me.

"Then let me present myself," he said. "I am Father Mario Gilano." Actually, I didn't get his name at all. Trudy had to fill me in later. But when I heard him say Father, I knew that meant he was a priest.

"I'm Trudy Baker and my friend is Rachel Jones. We're very pleased to meet you. I'm sure."

"Your names are very much American. Or what we think is American. Although your United States are a very mixed up people."

"You can say that again," I said.

"It must be terribly exciting to work here in a beautiful setting like this," Trudy rhapsodized. "But not

being Catholics we have no idea how the Vatican
works. I mean like," she fumbled, "exactly what do
you do? Everyone is going to ask us."

"We all work in *la Bottega del Papa*. That's the way
we call it."

Trudy explained that we would like very much to
see it and asked him to point it out to us on the map.
He seemed to think that was terribly amusing.

"That is just an expression I thought you knew. In
Italian it signifies the shop of the Pope."

"Languages are so confusing," I volunteered.

"Yes," said the priest.

A flight engineer told me that you could get tax-
free cigarettes and booze at the Vatican and the black
market traffic was terrific, but I didn't have the nerve
to ask him about that.

"Actually," he said, "my duties confine me largely
to the Vatican library."

I made a few comments as we strolled along together in the chapel, but soon realized Father Gilano
was more interested in Trudy and what she had to say.

"You know what?" I said, "I promised to meet
Jimmy Lane back at the hotel bar in ten minutes. I
have to run and leave you." Jimmy Lane was our
flight's engineer.

"What are you talking about?" Trudy asked, giving
me a strange look. "You didn't say anything about
meeting Jimmy."

"Yeah. Well, I forgot. Nice meeting you, Father.
So long." I walked away quickly, not even turning
back to answer Trudy's further protests. Trudy was
right in questioning my sudden date with Jimmy Lane.
I had no such date. But I did have a very strange
and uncomfortable feeling about Father Mario Gilano
and Trudy. There seemed to be a strong and unmis-
takable electricity between them, the kind I felt a few
times myself when I met someone new. I just had to

get away from the chapel and leave them alone. But once I set foot out on the streets of Rome, I began to regret my actions. Had I left my best friend in an awkward and embarrassing position by my sudden departure? I hoped not, and worried about it all the way back to the hotel.

In the hotel lobby I ran into Jimmy Lane. Before I could ask him to have a drink with me, he asked me for twenty thousand lire. I started fishing in my bag before I realized how much money that was. "I don't have that much with me. Let's have a drink and I'll cash a check."

"Let's cash the check first. I got a cab waiting," he said. He seemed jumpy. A young Italian boy in a waiter's jacket stood a few feet away, taking it all in.

"What's the matter, Jimmy, are you in some kind of trouble?"

"Let's cash the check, shall we?" he suggested.

When I headed for the desk, Jimmy tagged along behind. And the boy in the waiter's jacket tagged along behind him. I discovered I had to cash two twenty-dollar travelers' checks to assemble twenty thousand lire. Jimmy stood over me, helping me with my arithmetic, nervous as a guy trying to rob a bank. He counted the money twice. Then he handed it to the boy in the waiter's uniform. The boy counted it twice, smiled, put it in his pocket, bowed, said thank you very much, and disappeared. By that time we both needed a drink. We got a quiet table. He wanted to know where Trudy was.

"She's getting herself in trouble," I sighed.

"You kids have a tiff?"

"Not yet. We spent the afternoon at the Vatican."

"I wish I did." And then he told me he was minding his own business on the Via Veneto, watching all the girls go by, when he was approached by a man. "I didn't believe in this evil eye business, Rach, but these guys are wild. They read you like *that*. They read your mind and then, pow, they figure a way to take you."

"Tell me about it. I'm all ears."

"This guy leads me to a bar. He begins by giving me the lay of the land. Spoke English. Told me which girls were professionals and which ones weren't. He showed me how the police come by and the girls disappear. He told me to watch out for the English-speaking pimps. He suggested going to a little place around the corner. So, I agreed. He took me into this basement place. Two girls sat down at our table. They ordered drinks in Italian. When the waiter brought the order, he's got two bottles of champagne. I could see what was happening, so I wanted out. Right away they hand me a check for thirty thousand lire and I barely have ten on me. They say never mind, I can go back to the hotel to cash a check. So they send a waiter along with me. Listen, Rach, the Mafia's not all in New Jersey. There's quite a bit of it left over here."

I was about to order another drink when the waiter asked me if I was Miss Jones. I thought about it for a minute before I decided to confess. Then he told me I was wanted on the telephone. It was Trudy.

"Rachel," she said. "Where are you?"

"I'm in the bar having a drink with Jimmy Lane."

"That's what you said. But I thought you were fibbing."

"I was," I said. "But I'm not a very good liar. Sometimes the crazy things I say turn out to be true. Where are you?"

"Upstairs in our room. Dressing. Rach, you don't mind going the single route for tonight, do you?"

"No," I lied. "Why should I? What's up?"

"I have a dinner date, that's all."

"You didn't tell me," I said.

"It just happened," she said.

"Wonderful. Anybody I know?"

"Mario," she said.

"Mario?" I said. "I don't know any Mario."

"He's picking me up at six."

"Have a nice evening," I said. "I'll see you later."

"What are you going to do?" she asked.

"Tonight's my night to do volunteer work in the lobby. You know, for Travelers' Aid."

"Have you been drinking?"

"Yes," I said.

"Tell Jimmy to take good care of you," she said.

"He can't even take care of himself. Some Mafia guy just took him for 30,000 lire."

"Thirty thousand lire?" she said. "That's quite a take."

"It isn't the money so much, Trudy. It's the humiliation. So don't tell him I told you. Just watch these Italians. Mario included."

"I thought you liked him."

"Who?"

"Mario. Father Gilano."

"You're having dinner with *him?*" I sputtered. "He asked you to dinner?"

"You don't think I asked *him,* do you?"

"I don't know." I was sorry I'd asked. "I just didn't think priests went around asking girls for dates."

"OK, Rach, so he didn't come right out and ask me to dinner. I sort of led him into it. He's very nice, and I'm looking forward to talking to him and enjoying his company without the usual routine from a guy. He's very intellectual and polite and what's wrong with that?" She was getting herself into a huff.

"Have a nice time," I said.

"I will." She hung up.

I went back to the bar where Jimmy was waiting. We had another drink and then I paid the check. He wanted to know what was eating me, but I couldn't tell him. I couldn't make up any more stories. So I just told him Trudy was having dinner with a guy we met at the Vatican. Jimmy suggested we have dinner, but I begged off.

"Some other time, Jim," I said. "I'm going out and buy myself a present." Which I did. I went back to a little shop off the Via Veneto where I had seen this smashing high fashion knit. It would have cost a fortune at Bloomingdale's. By any standards, it was the most expensive dress I had ever bought, 'way over my head. But I was determined to punish myself.

It wasn't the money so much, it was the humiliation. I had thought of it first—how much fun it would be to have dinner for a change with a new kind of guy. How much fun it would be to be able to say I had picked up a handsome priest at the Vatican. I hadn't been scorned. But I had been passed over. And why? When I got back to the hotel I looked at myself in the mirror in my new outfit. I fooled around with my hair. Then it struck me. Trudy was darling and all that, but she was dark and tiny and cute. She could pass as the cousin of a priest. Or even his sister. But me? I wasn't the type. Not the type at all. Priests were rejoining the human race all right. You only had to read the papers to know that. But going out to dinner in Rome with willowy blondes in high-fashion get-ups? They weren't quite ready for that yet.

I decided to have a snack alone downstairs, pick up a juicy paperback at the newsstand and read myself into an early stupor. By seven o'clock I was in bed with *"The Godfather"* and a copy of the European edition of the *New York Times-Herald Tribune*. The book was such a hoot I hardly glanced at the paper. But I only had to skim the headlines to see it: A big picture of a handsome Italian-American, his

wife and two little boys. The first bride of a Roman
Catholic priest to write a book about it. And she
called it: *"I Married a Priest."* I raced through the
story. She said she was happy. She said for the first
years of their marriage priests and nuns used to call
them day and night asking for advice. Now nobody
calls. Now they just get married. I wondered if Trudy
had seen the story. Or Mario. Anyway, I tore out the
story and tossed the rest of the paper away. I took a
vow not to question Trudy about her evening. You
never find out anything by being nosey anyway. We'd
been flying together and rooming together and sharing
dates, laughs, perils, troubles. If she didn't want to
talk about it, that would be more significant than
anything she could possibly say. I would just shut up
and listen.

Trudy got in about ten. I said hello and then dived
into my book.

"How is it?" she asked.

"Excellent," I said. "How was your date?"

"I hate that word, Rachel."

"Excuse me," I said. "How was your rendezvous?"

"It wasn't a rendezvous. It was just a dinner en-
gagement."

"Look—in France when you have a rendezvous
with your dentist, it only means an appointment. Why
are you so defensive?"

"I'm not defensive."

"Date is a perfectly good four-letter word. We've
been flying together and rooming together, and sight-
seeing together, and dating together. And we usually
hash things over after an evening. We've practically
been confessionals for each other."

"That's a nasty word, Rachel," she said. "Just because I went out with a priest." She walked into the
bathroom and slammed the door.

That was it. I turned out my reading light and made a great show of going to sleep, replete with grunts and an instant snore.

Neither of us said anything until breakfast the next morning.

"I guess I acted pretty silly, Rach," Trudy said, munching on a sweet roll.

"I have no idea what you're talking about," I said, never looking up from my paper.

"Come on, Rach, I'm sorry. I'd love to tell you about last night."

"I'm not the least bit interested, Trudy. I'd much rather finish reading my newspaper."

"Come off it, Rachel. You can't read that paper. It's in Italian."

"There *are* pictures." I started giggling and so did Trudy and we were friends again. She told me all about dinner with Father Gilano. They'd eaten in a very tiny restaurant—Alfredo in Trastevere—and Father Gilano told Trudy of his boyhood and priesthood.

"He's so dedicated," she said as we went window-shopping along the Via Veneto. "And he talked about our society today and how its new morality puts an added strain on someone committed to God. Isn't that true, Rach? I mean, isn't that just the truth? He's a very deep man."

It was like a great big Chinese gong going off in my head. It seemed that I was destined to four days of suspicion of this relationship between my best friend and her Vatican acquaintance. Why had he brought up morality with Trudy? Was he looking for an opening in which to introduce more earthy matters than the Vatican library? Was Trudy being used by this young man to accomplish some long-standing need and desire?

"Gosh, Trudy, don't you think it's a little strange that he'd talk about morality the first time he met you?"

"What do you mean by that, Rachel Jones?"

"Nothing. Oh well, make a note in the diary that you had dinner your first night in Rome with a Vatican priest. It's a nice experience.".

"Yes, it is," said Trudy, admiring a leather pocketbook in a store window. "It'll be even nicer when I see him tonight."

"Again?"

"Yup. For dinner—only I'm treating this time. Young priests don't have much money, you know."

Trudy left for dinner that evening with Father Gilano while I went pub-crawling with a crew that had flown in that afternoon. By the time I got back to the hotel room, Trudy was sound asleep. As I undressed, I couldn't help noticing the little piece of paper on Trudy's night table. I picked it up and read it by the light coming in through the window. It was written in English. *Until tomorrow, in Eden. Mario.* I was shocked. There she lay, my closest friend, about to indulge in an affair with a priest. And there he was, a young Italian priest, about to break all his sacred vows. And he was flip and glib about it, too. Eden, indeed. Satan's Kingdom was more like it.

I tossed and turned all night. When I awoke, it was ten the following morning. I looked over and saw that Trudy's bed was empty. A note was pinned to the pillow. *Rachel—Will be gone all day and most of the night. See you tomorrow—Trudy.*

I spent the day sightseeing. I went to the Colosseum and the Roman Forum and thought of all the sacrifices and gladiators and blood. I wondered if I was walking where Julius Caesar walked. I sat on an ancient hunk of marble and wondered if Augustus ever sat there. And I never stopped wondering where Trudy was sitting that day. "As long as she's *sitting*," I told myself.

I went out with another flight crew that evening. We went to the old section of Rome and spent the evening listening to Italian folk songs and drinking Campari and soda. The crew's first officer was a doll, and we struck up a minor romantic relationship by the time we called it quits for the night. We made a date back in New York, kissed goodnight, and I fell into bed exhausted. Trudy still wasn't back and I thought about saying a little prayer for my best friend while falling asleep. I was going to pray for Father Gilano too, but I figured he could take care of himself in that department.

Trudy was in her bed when I awoke. I wanted very much to have a talk. She woke up at noon, adopted a maddening, pleasurable grin, sighed a few times and got up.

"Good morning, Miss Jones," she said, dancing around the room.

"It's true," I said with resignation.

"What's true, Rach?"

"What I figured was going on. I've seen you dance around a room only a few times, Trudy, and it was always the morning after a big night with somebody you fell in love with. But a *priest?*"

That started it all over again. I finally told Trudy I wanted only one hour with her in which we could discuss things without fighting or growing moody or defensive. She agreed to the hour, but told me she couldn't give me more than that because she was meeting *Mario* that afternoon for a tour of his library.

"What a gimmick," I blurted out. "Most men take you up to see etchings or stereo equipment, but this one invites you to his religious book collection."

"One more crack like that, Rachel, and not only will I not give you that hour but I'll never give you ten minutes of my time as long as I live." I decided to keep my cynicism to myself and waited patiently while Trudy bathed and dressed. We had lunch sent up, and the hour began. I could have strangled her when she checked her watch to establish a definite starting time.

"Go. You're on," she said, buffing her nails.

I spent the first ten minutes trying to re-establish our relationship as close friends. I assured her my only interest in the matter was for her best interests. I reminded her how many romances we'd been through together, the times we'd sat up all night discussing whichever particular romantic entanglement was taking place at the moment, the tears, the laughter at someone's impossibly awkward advances, the married men who'd appeared single. All this remembering of other times seemed to soften Trudy. By the time I was into my second quarter-hour, she was the same warm, open self I always knew.

"Trudy, can't you understand why I'm concerned?"

"No, I can't."

"You don't see the problems with having an affair with a Catholic priest?"

"Rachel, I am not having an affair with Father Gilano."

"But you're heading for it. I read his note to you about meeting you in the Garden of Eden."

Trudy laughed. "Dummy, he didn't say the Garden of Eden. He just said Eden—that's the name of the hotel where we met for lunch."

I was beginning to feel ridiculous, but pressed on.

"Did it ever occur to you that Father Gilano is falling in love with you?"

"No. Why should it?"

"Because he seems to want to spend every minute with you. Young men usually get that syndrome when they're falling in love with a girl. Right?"

"Right. But not in this case. He's just a warm and considerate man who enjoys talking with me. He told me last night how wonderful it is for him to be able to open up and speak freely with a woman. He said he's never done that before."

I smacked my head and paced the room.

"Trudy, has he ever tried to hold your hand?"

"Sure, whenever we're stepping over a puddle or some debris or some drunk in the street."

"Does he hang on to your hand after you've cleared the drunk?"

"I don't remember."

"Has he tried to kiss you?"

"On the cheek."

"When?"

"Last night. And the night before."

I smacked my head harder and walked faster in my circular path.

"Trudy Baker, this priest is fast falling in love with you, and you're not doing a thing to stop it. In fact, you're leading him right along the path."

Trudy sulked a little and attempted to bring the conversation to a close, but I wouldn't allow it. I looked at my watch. "Twenty-four minutes to go."

"You don't have to be so damned exact, Rach."

"Me, exact? You looked at your watch when we started."

"So what? I mean we've been friends long enough to not have to be so damned exact."

"Don't get me all wound up in a fight over the time," I said. "This hour is for discussing Father Gilano and you. Let's stick to that."

"All right."

"Trudy, if you pick up any paper or magazine or look at the best-seller list for books, you'll see just how big a thing it is these days for Catholic priests to think about leaving the church. Lots of them are getting married and leaving the priesthood. They even have an association for those who do. And do you know what problems it causes? Think about it, Trudy. Think about Father Gilano who's probably spent his whole life dreaming of becoming a priest. He becomes one, in the Vatican, yet. So along comes Miss Trudy Baker, mini-skirt and false eyelashes and sexy hips, and the poor, human guy takes one look and starts thinking things over. He falls in love. He decides to leave the church. You bat your eyes and say 'Gee whiz, isn't he groovy, and we'll really make something of all this!' So what happens? You two get married and he starts to feel guilty and it all ends up in one big mess where nobody is happy. Damn it, Trudy, it's like taking a guy away from his wife and family. To Father Gilano, the church is his family. It's his wife and kids all rolled into one. And frankly, as I check my watch and see that my allotted hour is coming to a close, you are, in my humble opinion, a bitch to allow all this to happen."

I plopped on my bed and waited for Trudy's purse to come sailing across the room. It would naturally strike me between the eyes and render me helpless for the rest of my life. Instead, Trudy came over to the bed, smiled at me and nodded. "Do you really think he's falling in love with me, Rach?"

"I can't be sure, buddy, but the chances are pretty good that he is."

"Maybe you're right. As far as I've been concerned, he liked me just because I was a good listener and gave him a chance to talk about things he never talks about with anyone else. But I'd hate to think I was making it hard for him to stay happy as a priest. It must be hard enough never loving a woman. Damn, damn, damn, Rachel. What do I do now?"

"We're leaving tomorrow," I said. "That ends it, I guess." I wasn't in the mood to suggest anything drastic.

"No, it won't end anything, Rach. He's coming to the States on business for the Vatican and we made a date in New York. In fact, he has relatives living in Philadelphia and he wants me to meet them."

"Beautiful. And you wonder if he's in love with you. For God's sake, Trudy, he's acting like a college guy taking the girl he's just pinned home to see momma. He'll probably propose tonight."

"What'll I do?"

We spent the afternoon discussing strategy. Trudy was determined not to hurt his feelings by telling him she didn't want to see him again. And she didn't want to make it appear she was acting in fear of the fact he'd fallen in love with her. "I mean, what if we're all wrong and he doesn't feel a thing for me except friendship. I'd look pretty silly telling him not to love me, when he didn't anyway."

We hadn't reached any conclusions by the time Trudy went to meet him. "I'll do something," she said as she climbed into a cab.

I sat up that night and waited for her to return. She walked in at midnight and obviously had been crying.

"Oh, Trudy," I said, putting an arm around her and sitting down on the edge of the bed. "What happened?"

"It's over," she cried.

"It was that bad?"

"No, not when I did it. I didn't start to cry until I was in the cab coming back here."

"What did you say?"

"I told him I had to leave dinner early because a

pilot with the airline, the one who fathered my illegitimate child, was in Rome. I told him I had to see him to collect the money he pays me to keep the whole affair quiet from his wife. I told him it was an accident and that I never forget to take my birth control pills any more. I told him I could just never get enough of sex and supposed I was a nymphomaniac or something."

I was speechless. When I finally was able to compose a question, Trudy had gotten up and was already into her pajamas.

"What did *he* say, Trudy?" I dreaded hearing the answer.

"What did he say? He smiled at me, told me he didn't know whether to believe me or not, but got the message anyway. He blessed me in case I was telling the truth, kissed me on the cheek in case I wasn't telling the truth and was just trying to head off something dangerous, got me a cab and said goodbye."

"Did he mention New York?"

"Yes. He said he really didn't like his relatives in Philadelphia anyway, and was going to cancel his trip to the States, and go into retreat."

"Whew," I went. "It must have been tough, but at least it's over."

"Yeah. The big problem is that now I don't believe he really was falling in love with me. I really don't."

"He knows, Trudy."

CHAPTER XV

"Jim and Alice"

Airline captain Jim Moore pulled himself out of bed and shivered. He'd spent much of the previous night with his accountant; bookkeeping errors kept popping up in the operation of Jim's two frozen custard stands, and the pizza-slice stores were showing less profit than the year before. Sometimes, on mornings like these, Jim Moore wondered if it was worth having business ventures on the side. But all airlines pilots had them, and Jim knew it was only right that he, too, should practice free enterprise in the moonlight.

He shuffled into the bathroom, grabbing his pajama bottoms just before they slipped to the floor. He shivered again as he walked across the tile floor. The season had turned from summer to early fall, and it was time for heat. He'd take care of that as soon as he got back from this trip.

Jim took off his pajama top and looked at himself in the mirror. He groaned and quickly turned his eyes to the sink and the steam rising from the hot water. He hated to see himself in the morning, or any time, for that matter. He looked in the mirror again and noticed his stomach seemed to be sagging even more than the morning before. Of course, Jim was aware that when a man reached his forties, that sagging increased. But he was sure it was more pronounced on him than it should be. Even his chest was beginning to sag. If only he'd gotten more sun that summer; sagging frames always looked less saggy with a tan. His pasty-white body accented the loss of muscle control.

And there was the matter of Jim's face. The beard was turning grey in spots. Under the chin, the flesh was beginning to loosen up, which made the rest of his face look thinner. His hair, thin and graying, was like straw in the wind. Lately, Jim had found himself sleeping with his arms folded over his head, which he was certain would hasten the balding process and most definitely made his hair more difficult to manage. Being tall—six feet—was good, because few people saw the bald crown on his head. But he knew it was there from holding a hand mirror to catch his reflection from the big mirror over the sink.

"You're really a mess, old man," He pulled the razor across his cheek. "Oh, hell," he muttered, feeling the blade's dull edge as it tried to yank the whiskers out by the roots. Jim's wife, Martha, had used his razor and ruined the blade. He changed blades and cut his lip in two places. After taking down the stockings, panties and bras hanging on the shower curtain rod, he got into the tub. Some of the tile was beginning to loosen, the cascading water getting behind the tiles and sending a stream of dirt out through the cracks. Tiles in a six-year-old, 85-thousand dollar house in Connecticut shouldn't be loose so soon. Jim was sure of that. He got out of the tub, dried, and splashed his face with lime after-shave lotion, some of it getting into his left eye and burning. His pajama bottoms did fall as he reached the bedroom, causing him to trip and knock a large lamp from a table.

"Will you please be quiet, Jim?" Martha grumbled.

"I'm sorry, dear, but I tripped and couldn't help it."

"Well, have a little consideration. Others are trying to sleep."

"Yes, dear."

He fumbled around trying to find socks, shorts and a uniform shirt. It was impossible in the dark, and he knew Martha would be upset if he turned on any lights. He decided to slip into a pair of painting pants he found in the corner of the closet. He got back into his slippers and left the bedroom, tripping over the dog on the way. The dog growled in contempt.

"Jim, please," Martha said from the bed.

"Sorry, sorry."

Downstairs he put on the coffee pot and went into the garage to get a flashlight to aid in dressing. Oil was leaking from the rear of his Volkswagen. "Goddam it," he said to the car. It would mean taking Martha's Pontiac station wagon to the airport, which would send her into a fit of depression.

He came back into the kitchen to discover he'd pushed the wrong button on the stove. The oven was on. The coffee pot was cold. He'd also left the flashlight in the garage. He retrieved it, the door slamming behind him. The dog barked upstairs and Martha yelled. Jim pushed the right button and got the coffee going. He opened the refrigerator and saw there was no milk. Or cream. With a stomach full of ulcers, as Jim was sure was the case, black coffee could not be tolerated first thing in the morning.

Jim Moore sat down at the kitchen table and hung his head in his hands. It was all too much, even for the captain of a multi-million dollar jet. There he was, about to command his first flight to Tokyo, and he couldn't even manage to perform the simple task of beginning a day. Jim Moore was a failure as a man; a hell of a jet captain, but a human flop.

While this early morning tale of Americana was taking place in Connecticut, another scene was being played in Manhattan. There, in a high-rise apartment building on the East Side, Alice Richmond swung at the alarm clock beside the bed and sent it tumbling to the floor. The next thing she swung at was the cat, a stray found two months ago in front of the Unitarian Church. It was rubbing up against her face as a signal that food would be appreciated.

"Dumb cat," Alice said, pushing the animal off the bed. "Oh, poor kitty," she said reaching over and pulling it back up and cuddling against it. "I'm sorry. You're the best friend I have, kitty. You really are."

The cat purred and exercised its claws on the blanket.

Alice managed to get to a sitting position on the side of the bed and stretch her legs. She looked down at her feet and reconfirmed her belief that they were ugly feet. She got up and put on water in the pullman kitchen for instant coffee. The kettle eventually whistled. There was no coffee. Just boiling water. Not even a tea bag. She'd have to remember to steal some from the plane. She sat down and started a list of things she needed, all available from the aircraft's galley.

"Tokyo," she sighed, stepping into the shower and turning on the water. It was cold. It had been cold for three days, despite the super's promise to have it fixed. The cold needles of water drove chills into her body, a tall, lanky one with only slight protrusions where an airline stewardess's globular, ample breasts were supposed to be. She looked down and silently cursed her knobby knees. "Enough!" she said to the faucet spewing out the ice water. She dried herself and took a long, hard look in a full-length mirror. "Ugh," she said, poking a finger into her belly. She turned and examined her back. She saw hips and a rump too heavy for a tall, thin girl. She thought of all the other nude female bodies she'd seen in two years of stewardessing, and ranked herself at the bottom of the list. All this displeasure with her appearance had not kept Alice Richmond from enjoying the normal pursuit of the pleasures of young life, although she was certain she enjoyed less than the other girls. She was in the midst of a ho-hum affair with a young ad executive who seemed to enjoy the few times they went to bed but never said so. She'd mentioned to him the first time that her breasts were small and he replied with that dreadful line, "Anything over a handful's a waste." Jerk. I don't think I'll see him again, she promised herself, slipping into panties and going back to the kitchen for a bowl of corn flakes. She poured the cereal and milk and started to eat when the phone rang. It was the ad executive.

"Morning, baby."

"Why are you calling this early?"

"Look, don't give me any jazz about early calls. I'm calling to invite you to my place for the night. We'll just make it a real Madison Avenue orgy. Notches on the bed and all. We'll run it up the bedpost and see who makes it. How's that sound, sweets?"

Alice couldn't find the right words. She wanted to say he only wanted her for sex and her body, but she knew that would get a laugh. She hung up. Hard. She hated him. She probably wouldn't hate him so much if her period had arrived on time. But it was two days overdue and damn him if she were pregnant. Damn her.

She went back to the kitchen and found the cat finishing the corn flakes. She didn't even scold it. She drank orange juice and continued getting dressed, turning recent bills from Bloomingdale's, Peck and Peck, Saks, Macy's and Best and Company face down so the amounts wouldn't be visible. Alice decided she was miserable. Life's misfortune. Better dead than in the red. Tokyo. With Captain Jim Moore. Better Paris with a near-sighted swinger.

Back in Connecticut, Jim Moore had pulled his head from his hands and had gone to the bedroom. He felt so low, so depressed. He flicked on the flashlight and trained its beam into a dresser drawer. The shorts. The sky blue shorts with the little airplane on them, like the alligator on a golfer's shirt. He slipped out of his painting pants and into the shorts. They fit right. He felt a little better. Next came the socks, long, black over-the-calf ones. Neat. The T-shirt tapered for a slimming effect. And then the uniform itself. The trousers first, good-looking blue with a trace of a stripe down the sides. Tapered blue shirt. Dark blue tie with a small, neat knot. And then the jacket, matching the pants, shoulder pads, gold stripes around the sleeves and with the wings, the big set of gold wings, perfectly aligned on the breast. He felt the precious bodily fluids surge through his veins. He grabbed the hat, crushed just so, placed it squarely on his head with just enough gray temple showing, and marched from the bedroom.

"You bastard," he whispered to the dog. The dog looked up and panted, laughed really, and wagged his tail. Respect. Jim Moore patted his head and went to the kitchen where he wrote Martha a note telling her why he took the station wagon. He took one last look at himself in the hall mirror and smiled. He gave a short jab at the mirror with his fist, winked at himself and set off for the drive to the airport.

On Manhattan's East Side, Alice Richmond hooked on her padded bra and checked the mirror. Better. The panty hose felt sensual as she slipped into them and adjusted them to her body. The knobby knees were covered. The slip was new and expensive. And then the sky-blue skirt. The pale blue blouse, freshly laundered. The jacket, pert and cute and cut so perfectly. The wings looked better on a larger girl, Alice told herself. And she could carry the cap nicely, nestled there in her hair. Before, that hair had been a drab and dismal brown. Now, it shone with sexual radiance. She gathered up her raincoat, picked up her small suitcase, and marched from the apartment. Alice hailed a sleepy cab driver.

"Lovely day, isn't it?" she said, getting into the cab.
"Yes, ma'am."

Captain Jim Moore noticed Alice enter Operations and smiled a greeting. They'd flown together before and, frankly, never really got along that well. Jim thought Alice very attractive. He liked her smile and her hair and the way she carried herself. He often engaged her in conversation but she seemed more polite than interested.

For Alice, Captain Jim Moore represented a special case in her relationships with airline captains. She liked him, in fact felt strong sexual urges at times when she talked with him in the cockpit. She, of course, didn't know that he often projected thoughts of her into a motel bed, and had even dreamed of her on occasion. Once, he woke up in the middle of the night saying her name over and over. Martha woke up, too.

"Who's Alice?" she demanded.

"Oh, just that crazy song the kids like, I guess. You know. Alice's Resturant. I heard it a lot today," Jim told his wife, pleased at how quickly he could lie in such a stupor.

"Well, please keep quiet, Jim. I'm trying to sleep."

"OK, hon."

Captain Moore taxied the big 707 out to the active runway at Kennedy Airport, received his clearance from the tower and pushed the four throttles to maximum power. The plane rolled down the runway and was soon airborne, heading for Tokyo, via Honolulu. Once the course was set on the assigned jetway, the cockpit crew could sit back, relax, and pass the time with idle conversation. It was the same in the rear of the plane where the four stewardesses had settled the light load of passengers into the initial stages of the flight and had an hour before serving breakfast.

"You ever make it with the girl in the back, Jim?" the first officer asked Jim Moore.

"Which one?"

"The tall one. Alice."

"No."

"I'm surprised. She really has the hots for you."

"Don't be silly."

"I'm not being silly. Everybody knows it."

Jim shook his head and laughed. He wished it were true. But he was sure it wasn't. Not a girl like Alice. She probably fought off the boys and had all the affairs she could handle. Sure, Jim Moore knew he was one hell of a handsome airline captain, with that great blue uniform and wrinkles from squinting into the sun at 40,000 feet. Everybody knew he was a virile and attractive captain. Sure, he never played around because . . . well, just because the whole routine of getting into a motel with a girl and having to take off your uniform and display your weaknesses didn't appeal to him. Of course, nobody had to know that. Let them think he was a lover. What they didn't know wouldn't hurt them.

"I mean it, Jim," the first officer was saying. "All you'd have to do would be snap your fingers and that girl would roll over for you."

"Sure. Well, maybe I'll snap 'em tonight," Jim quipped, deliberately turning his attention to enroute charts.

In the rear, Alice Richmond kicked off her shoes and stood in the galley with another stew, Sharon Lewis.

"Alice?"

"What?"

"Have you ever been to bed with Captain Moore?"

"Nope."

"Come on, you can tell me."

"I know I can. And I haven't—been to bed with Captain Moore."

"It must break his heart," Sharon said, pouring them coffee.

"Why?"

"Come on, Alice. Just look at him when he sees you coming. He almost drools. He's got a real thing for you."

"He's married."

"How about that?"

"What?"

"Big deal. So he's married. He's also human, and he gets his most human look when you're around."

The light came on in the galley, indicating a passenger wanted something. Alice slipped into her shoes and left the galley. She got the passenger the blanket he wanted, but her mind was on the cockpit. It was ridiculous to think Captain Jim Moore would want *her*. Nonsense. He was a very handsome airline captain and probably fought off the girls in every city. She thought back to the other trips with him and remembered he was never part of the gang that went to dinner and haunted the nightclubs. Of course not. He was back in bed with his girl in that particular port. Actually, Jim Moore always carried a good book with him and spent every evening away from home reading. Alice didn't know that. Nor did Jim Moore know that Alice seldom lasted long with the gang in destination cities. Once she got out of her uniform and changed into civilian clothes, she lost interest and confidence. Usually she, too, read in the motel. Gothics. Her favorites. And an occasional spicy novel for vicarious pleasure.

The flight arrived in Tokyo at four in the afternoon. The crew checked into their hotel, showered, rested, and prepared to go out for a night on the town. They wouldn't be able to drink because their return flight was scheduled to depart at five the following afternoon. Air line crews are prohibited from drinking within 24 hours of a flight. However, just before the crew left the hotel for dinner, the maintenance chief at the airport called Captain Moore.

"We did a power run-up on that number four engine, captain, like you requested. It's all fouled up. We're gonna pull it now and take a look. But I think the fan's shot and we don't stock them here. We'll have to get one flown in tomorrow."

Captain Moore thanked the chief, told him to check it and to expect a call in a few hours. Everyone left the hotel secretly hoping the engine was unfixable, allowing more time in Tokyo.

They had dinner at France-ya, listed as a French restaurant in guide books but actually a superb steak house serving the best of Japanese beef, which also happens to be the best beef in the world. Everyone ordered *chabu chabu,* thin beef cooked in hot broth by the individual, with plenty of beef falling into the kettle due to the crew's sloppy chopstick technique. Captain Moore called operations at the airport after dinner and got the bad, or good, news. The engine would have to be replaced. That gave the crew until nine the morning following the day of scheduled departure. And that meant drinking was on-limits until nine the next morning. *Sake* was ordered, and everyone began to loosen up and enjoy the evening. Everyone except Jim Moore and Alice Richmond.

"Boy, you two look beat," Sharon Lewis said, poking Alice in the ribs. "Why don't you both go back to the hotel and get a good night's sleep?"

"Yeah," the first officer concurred. "Good idea, Jim. You look like you could use some rest."

Jim and Alice glanced nervously at each other. They offered a few protests, but the rest of the crowd became more insistent. Finally Jim and Alice agreed they were tired, and left together. They took a cab, sitting far apart in the rear seat while the driver performed his suicide mission. His passengers clung desperately to their respective door handles to prevent sliding against each other. Jim unbuttoned his shirt collar and tried to get comfortable. His suit, a summer wash 'n wear, began to feel sloppy and cumbersome. He caught a glimpse of himself in the rear view mirror and sadly noted his hair looked thin and uncombed. His jowls seemed more pronounced.

Alice also felt uncomfortable, not only at their silence but at her appearance. Her dress was a summer cotton, cut too full as far as Alice was concerned. But so what? Her figure didn't show off any of her civilian clothes the way they should be displayed, anyway. Any old thing was fine. She sat in the cab wishing she were in uniform.

Jim Moore, desperate for the right thing to say, offered to buy Alice a drink in the hotel bar. She accepted, claiming to have a headache and not being properly dressed but willing for one fast nightcap to help her sleep.

"That's the way I feel, too," Jim said, holding open the cocktail lounge door. They took a quiet table in the rear of the lounge, ordered Ballantine Scotch and soda, and silently sipped. They were suffering identical emotions and thoughts. Both found it extremely pleasant being there together. Both allowed their minds to wander towards a possible sexual climax to the evening. And both felt deep insecurity.

They finished their drinks and made shuffling motions in their chairs, indicating the night was over. But Jim surprised himself. "How about another drink, Alice?"

"I guess so."

They talked a little over the second drink. By the time they were finishing their fourth Scotch and soda, they were giddy and loose. Jim told jokes and Alice laughed. She told about the cat eating her corn flakes and Jim told dog stories.

"How about one last drink in my room?" he asked brazenly.

"Sure. Love it."

Both got up from the table a little unsteadily. Jim paid the check and took Alice's arm. They continued to tell stories as they passed through the lobby and rode alone in the elevator. Jim led her to his room, fished for the key, found it, opened the door and took Alice's hand. He guided her to the large windows that looked out over Tokyo's neon spectacular. Slowly, Jim took Alice in his arms. He heard her sigh—more of a "cooo"—and kissed her lightly on the lips. She responded warmly, leading Jim to press further. His hands began to wander up and down her back, eventually dipping down lower to the curve of her fanny. She melted into his arms and turned slightly. Jim adjusted to her shift in position. He was now facing a large, gilt-edged mirror on the wall. It was like a slap of reality across the face. He loosened his grip on Alice and cleared his throat. "I think . . . I . . . How about that drink, Alice?" His voice had risen an octave. As he broke away, Alice caught a fast glance at herself in the same mirror and felt dejected. She readily accepted the drink, relieved to curl up in the chair and hide behind herself.

"Take off your shoes," Jim offered.

"No."

The new infusion of alcohol acted in concert with the old, bringing relative calm to the couple. Alice started talking about her childhood and the phobias she had. Jim was a good listener, and eventually began offering insight into his own life. They talked freely until three in the morning.

"I'd better get to bed," Alice said, getting up from the protective shell she'd created in the chair.

"Me, too."

"Goodnight, Jim. Thanks for the drinks and talk."

"Oh, sure. My pleasure. Uh, Alice, would you consider having dinner tomorrow night with me? I mean, just the two of us?"

"I'd love that, Jim."

Alice undressed quietly to avoid waking Sharon. She got into bed and browsed through the daily newspaper, compliments of the hotel. She didn't pay much attention to anything in the paper, her thoughts fixed on Jim Moore and their evening together. She was about to close the paper and turn off the lights when the advertisement caught her eye.

AMERICAN VISITORS—LEARN THE ART OF THE GEISHA. PRIVATE LESSONS—BE HAPPY AND FREE AS GEISHA—LOW PRICES—SATISFACTION GUARANTEED

Alice laughed at her interest in the ad and tossed the paper on the floor. She clicked off the bed lamp and closed her eyes.

Jim Moore also had turned to the newspaper for some last-minute relaxation before sleeping. He saw the same ad for geisha instruction. He also noticed another ad run by the same geisha school.

AMERICAN BUSINESSMAN—TIRED? NERVOUS? COME AND RELAX WITH BEST GEISHA GIRLS IN TOKYO—PRIVATE SESSIONS—SATISFACTION GUARANTEED

"These Japanese are really something," he muttered to himself, closing the paper and getting into bed. "You've got to give them credit. They know how to live."

Alice was already dressed when Sharon woke up. "Where were *you* last night?" Sharon asked.

"With Jim Moore."

"See? I knew it would end up this way."

"It didn't end up any way, Sharon. We just talked."

"About what?"

"Nothing in particular."

"You seeing him again?"

"Tonight. We're having dinner."

"Where are you going, Alice? It's so early."

"Just out. I just feel like a long walk alone."

"Have fun. See you tonight."

"OK, Sharon." Alice left the room, yesterday's newspaper snugly under her arm.

Down the hall, Jim Moore was showered and shaved. He nibbled at his breakfast and looked at the ad in the paper. "Why not?" he asked himself. "Maybe this is just what I need to build a little confidence in myself." He dialed the number and made a three-hour appointment—noon to three that afternoon.

Alice called the number in the ad from a lobby phone booth. She made her appointment for ten that morning. And to get the full benefit from the instruction, she booked five hours—ten to three. Lunch would be served, she was told.

The Tokyo School of Geisha Gaiety occupied an impressive Oriental building just off the Ginza. The gaping mouth of a dragon formed the entrance. Once inside the mouth, a student was led to a typical Japanese room with mats on the floor and a low table in the middle.

"Welcome, Miss Richmond," the school's director said as she settled Alice into the room. She was a middle-aged woman, very pretty, and wearing the traditional kimono of the geisha.

"This school, Miss Richmond, is mostly for teaching the young Japanese girl to be the geisha. They come to me when they are sixteen and study many years before they are able to join the union and work as geisha in Tokyo. For our visitors from the west, we try to give just the taste of being a geisha so the lady will be better able to make her man happy."

Alice said she understood, and was left alone to change into a kimono and await her instructor, a lovely Japanese girl named Kiki. Kiki showed Alice how to serve tea gracefully, how to listen to stories and smile, how to act coy, or bold, and how to perform simple flower arranging. Everything, of course, was abbreviated and simple. But it was the general atmosphere and mood that was catching. Alice began to feel like a highly-trained and lovely female, one fully prepared to serve a man with grace and pleasure. Kiki served lunch in the traditional geisha manner. Then, at two, she informed Alice that each geisha should know something of the bath ritual. Alice agreed, and Kiki led her to the bath area.

"Please to take off clothes," Kiki said. Alice slipped out of her kimono. "First," Kiki said, "man like to have all evil and bad nerves go from his body. He like room with steam. You go in steam room and see." Alice had been in sauna baths before, so the steam room was nothing new. She sat in it a few minutes before Kiki beckoned her back into the dressing room.

"Now, Miss Richmond, man should be clean before enjoying bath. You wash him from bucket here. Use brush. And much soap. I show." Kiki scrubbed Alice down with the stiff brush. At first, it hurt. But she soon became used to it, and enjoyed the stimulation on her skin.

"Now, Miss Richmond, is time for bath. Here in Japan, we do not be ashamed of taking the bath. Here in Japan, man and woman take bath together. All together in *big* bath. Come. I show you."

Kiki led Alice through a curtain and into the actual bath area. Alice had never seen anything quite like it before. There were at least a dozen people in the huge, sunken pool. Three or four Japanese women were in the group. No one seemed to pay any attention to anyone else. A few of the men talked as they soaked in the steaming hot water, but it was all very casual.

"You go in water now, Miss Richmond," Kiki insisted.

Alice felt an unusual calm come over her. Of course

she would go in and take her bath with everyone else. It was the custom, and everyone accepted it as part of life. The body was part of you. It was beautiful. It was useful. It was nothing to be ashamed of.

Still, you couldn't expect an American girl with knobby knees and a flat chest to go bounding into the water with abandon. You had to expect a little reserve, if only out of fear of the boiling water. So Alice Richmond carefully began to back into the big tub. She winced as her feet were assaulted by the scalding water, and stood there a few minutes until the skin had gotten used to the temperature, or dropped off. She backed in a little further. Kiki giggled, her dainty face covered with a rice paper fan. Soon, Alice had gotten into the water up to her hips. It was beginning to feel good. A Japanese gentleman, an older man, bowed a greeting to her. Alice quickly brought her arms up to cover her breasts. The man just turned away and went back to splashing water over the back of another man. Alice backed further into the tub. The water came up over her hips, covered her waist and soon reached her chest. She was completely relaxed. She even managed the courage to look around a little. Not far. Not behind her. To the sides. If she had turned and looked behind, she would have seen the naked Jim Moore backing across the tub. His geisha, after washing him and attending to him in the steam room, had led him to the pool. For Jim, the hot water was the major drawback to plunging in freely, although his nakedness played a part, too. He noticed a large Japanese lady and her husband in the pool as he backed past them, and smiled. Wasn't it nice for a man and wife to enjoy a bath together? Jim took a deep breath and felt his tension drain into the hot water. He was a man, without any help from his uniform. He would take Alice Richmond to dinner, conquer her and sweep her into bed, proudly displaying his masculine body by strutting around the room. Never again would he depend upon his uniform for strength. Never.

Alice was enjoying similar thoughts. She was projecting ahead to evening when, she decided, she would flirt Jim Moore's pants off at dinner, suggest they go to his room, fling off her clothes, stretch her arms to the heavens and let him ravage her body with his eyes. "A free woman," she said, realizing the older Japanese man was looking at her. Alice smiled at him. Alice looked over and smiled at Kiki. She smiled back. Alice shook her hair and rubbed the hot water on her breasts. And then she took another step back. So did Jim. She felt her rump touch another rump, a harder one. A MAN! Alice turned to stone.

Jim felt the softness of a woman's fanny touch his rear end. His reaction was different. A Japanese woman. Pleasant. He wouldn't be slapped. This was what it was all about. He would turn and say hello to her. He was Jim Moore, airline captain, lover, and naked free spirit.

Alice forced herself to not panic over bumping into a man in the tub. She would turn and smile at the Japanese man whose rump was nestled against hers. She turned.

Jim turned.

"Captain Moore!"

"Miss Richmond!"

"What are you doing here?" Alice asked.

"Taking a bath."

"Me, too."

It was Jim Moore who started to laugh. Alice joined in, and soon they were hysterical in the water, tears running from their eyes as they looked at each other and analyzed the situation. Jim gingerly reached out and took Alice's hand. He led her through the water, up the shallow steps to Kiki.

"Miss Richmond would like to dress now," he said.

Kiki bowed. "I'll meet you in the dragon's mouth in ten minutes," he told Alice. Her eyes met his and she understood.

Twenty minutes later, Jim and Alice were between the sheets in Jim's room. He was kissing her knee while she kissed the balding crown of his head.

"You're lovely, Alice Richmond," he said. "Every inch of you, from head to toe."

"Toe, too?"

"All ten."

They made love for the rest of the afternoon and evening. The next morning, at six, Alice crept back to her room, showered, dressed in her uniform and was ready to go to the airport with the crew. Sharon Lewis didn't ask any questions. The cockpit crew didn't probe Jim, either. The flight back to New York was uneventful. The crew signed out in Operations and went their respective ways. Jim walked Alice to the line of cabs where she would catch one for Manhattan. His car, the station wagon, was parked in the employees' parking lot.

"Thanks, Alice," Jim said.

"For what?"

"For everything. It's too complicated to explain."

"Well, don't try, then. But thanks from me, too."

"Sure. Well, see you next week. You're working New York-Tokyo all month aren't you?"

"Yup."

"Well, I'll see you, then."

"OK, Jim. So long."

He watched her slide into the cab and be driven off towards the city. He walked to his car and headed to Connecticut. He knew that once he got home and changed out of his uniform, nothing would really be different. It would be the same for Alice. But in the hot baths of Tokyo, there was no need for uniforms or wings or anything else to be used as a prop. Jim Moore was a man. And Alice Richmond was a woman.

CHAPTER XVI

"Contributing to the Delinquency of an Asian Minor"

Philadelphia has always been that any-old-port-in-a-storm town to me. When Kennedy Airport was hopelessly snowed in, fog-bound, or jammed with stacked aircraft waiting to land, the worst thing that might happen was to be ordered to Liberty Bellsville for a landing. That only happened to us once. We came in by train and discovered it was only an hour something out of New York. Philadelphia is one of the oldest cities in America. Its name reeks of so much ancient American history I had no idea there was another Philadelphia. I found out, the hard way.

And I got there, the hard way, on a two-engine Fairchild.

I was always on the lookout for antiques, but this was ridiculous. When I saw the initials T H Y on the aircraft I wondered what they stood for. When you wonder things out loud you sometimes get an answer. In English, too.

"That means to hell with you," the ticket agent smiled.

"Let's stay here in Athens like we planned," Trudy said to me when she heard that.

The man assured us we need have no fear. This was a regular run of the Turkish National Airline, and all their pilots were military fliers trained by the American Air Force and NATO. "Turkey?" I said with some surprise. "Why are we traveling on a Turkish airline to get to Asia Minor? Philadelphia, the old original one, was supposed to be in Asia Minor. In ruins, practically."

"Asia Minor is sometimes called Turkey," the man said. "Or vice versa." Which shows you how much geography we learned in Stew School. I had the idea Asia Minor was a legendary ruin like the Lost Continent of Atlantis. Not quite under water, maybe, but close to it, waiting for one more earthquake to decide things.

"Let's stay in Athens like we planned," Trudy kept insisting. She had some kind of premonition about a disaster. Now it seemed to be centered on the plane we were about to board. We had come to Athens with plans for a lovely four-day layover. Since Greece seemed to be on the edge of another revolution, we hoped something exciting might develop during our stay. And sure enough, it did. The first friend we called was on his way to a big cocktail party at the Hilton in Athens and insisted we come along. It was the kind of party we love. There seemed to be three men for every woman and from the moment we made our entrance we were swamped with attention. It was a real smorgasbord of male types: Austrian archeologists, American writers, Italian engineers, a French photographer, British businessmen, American Army and Navy officers, Dutch diamond merchants, American tobacco buyers, all on the loose and looking for action.

"Don't tie yourself up until we've played the field," Trudy cautioned me. So we fenced and tried to keep moving, trying to wade through the aggressive types and not commit ourselves. "I'm sorry," I kept saying, after we got separated, "I'm with friends." Whenever we collided, we would compare notes. "Promise them anything" was our axiom, as long as it was for tomorrow.

Trudy was smitten with a U. S. Naval Commander who claimed he was unattached. Trudy felt he was married and she wanted me to check him over with my radar. When I got a good look at him I decided the whole thing was irrelevant. He was so attractive. "If he feels free and claims he's free, why are you so suspicious?" I scolded her. I was partial to an Austrian archeologist because I had never met one before. His hair was a little thin on top, but otherwise he looked like something off a travel poster, a real sensitive Storm Trooper. I was giving him my undivided attention when a tall, dark man moved in and introduced himself. His name was Marc, and I could tell he was French by his accent and because he stood so close I could barely breathe.

He asked me if I were a mannequin, which I thought was kind of cute. I had suffered to diet away about seven pounds of bloat and I was thrilled to think it might show. "I'm not nearly skinny enough for *that*," I said. "But thanks anyway."

He persisted in asking me what I was doing in Athens. I knew if I didn't tell him somebody else would, so I confessed to being one of the jet set who worked for a living.

"The reason I asked is because I am in need of an American girl," he said.

It was a cute and plaintive proposition. When I asked him why, he explained he was a photographer who traveled all over shooting pictures for *Paris Match* and *Life* and *Look* and also for himself. I thanked him but said I had an experience in Copenhagen which cured me permanently and forever of having anything to do with anybody who worked behind a lens. When I told him my Danish stories he didn't seem to be discouraged at all.

"I am sure you enjoyed it as an experience, no matter how much you deny it," he said. "There is no reason why you should not enjoy going on location with me to Philadelphia."

This was the way I got into trouble. I promised to do it if it would fit into my schedule. You see, I thought he was talking about doing a little job for him in America. I thought that could be fun. When I discovered he was talking about a Philadelphia that was only an hour away, I was afraid to admit I was such a ninny about geography. So I listened some more. An American agency in Paris had sent down two girls for him. He didn't like them and sent them away. "I wanted a much more ordinary girl," he told me.

"Thank you very much," I said, trying to act as if he had insulted me. But I understood what he meant. When I checked with Trudy she happened to be in a very commercial mood. She wanted to know how much he was willing to pay. When I asked him, he got very generous. He invited Trudy and me and her American Naval Commander to have dinner with him. The more we talked, the more committed I felt and the more fun he made it seem. A 48-hour jaunt to the ruins of Asia Minor. Twelve hours work for him and maybe two hours work for us and the chance to get paid for seeing some of the most ancient sights in the world. Marc went ahead on an early flight with an assistant and made arrangements for us to meet him at the Grand Hotel in Ephesus. Now, we were at the Athens Airport thinking of backing out simply because the plane was antique.

"We're always hearing about the good old days," I finally told Trudy. "Let's see what was good about them."

We climbed into the tiny Fairchild with only about thirty other passengers, mostly men. That's one thing about traveling east. The further you go, the better the odds.

The T H Y stewardess might have been a Turkish delight on the ground, but on our airline she would have been called in and ordered to drop at least fifteen pounds. Her shape might have been sensational in a belly dancer's outfit, but in a short jacket and straight skirt she was all hills and valleys. The men seemed to appreciate her, though, as she lunged down the narrow aisle serving them what turned out to be warm lemonade.

Trudy made such a face when she tasted it that a man across the aisle unfastened his seat belt and moved into the empty spot next to her. It wasn't nearly as vomitous as she made out. She was playing the damsel in distress. And, if I may say so, slightly overdoing it.

"What you need is a spot of this," he suggested, unscrewing the top of a very chic, thin, Moroccan-bound flask.

"*That* is supposed to be lemonade," he said. "*This* is guaranteed 100 proof vodka."

He poured for both of us. It made a very palatable mixture. Then he moved in with all the standard gambits. Was this our first trip to Turkey? Didn't we know that one should never take to the hills or the skies of Muslim lands without an emergency supply of spirits? He reminded us that the Muslims frowned on alcohol and on some airlines in the Middle East there was a no-drink limit. The planes might smack of the fifties, but the hip flask was taking us back to the twenties.

"I've made this trip at least fifty times," he explained. "But I still need an anesthetic for the landing at Ismir."

"Is the airport dangerous?" we wondered. The weather was calm and clear.

"It's not the airport, it's these young Turk sky-jockeys," he said, shuddering and taking another swig. "You'll see."

We sure did. At a certain point, after the sign ordered us to fasten our seat belts, my purse hurtled off the seat. The bottom dropped out of everything as we took what seemed to be a vertical dive straight down.

Being in the window seat, I was on my own. When I straightened up to catch my breath, I saw Trudy being held securely in the arms of this gallant American and not minding it a bit. When we finally landed we finished the poor man's vodka as the plane taxied in to the ramp.

You could tell he was very much at home in this part of the country; all the officials seemed to defer to him. He asked us where we were headed. When we told him the Grand Hotel of Ephesus he smiled and said, "That's my second home. Stick with me."

We got into a taxi. The driver seemed to know him. He bowed politely, smiled, bared beautiful teeth under a huge hippy-type moustache and said: "Good morning, General Taylor. Would you like a Coca Cola?"

Our friend just laughed.

Well, I thought, Miss Baker knew what she was doing playing the lady in distress. I would never have guessed that this gallant American was a general. He must certainly have been the youngest general anywhere, actually young enough to be single. I wondered if he was in the Air Force or the Army. Somehow, he didn't sound like a pilot.

"You can call me Doug," he said.

"Doug Taylor," Trudy said. "There's a nice American name. What part of the states are you from?"

"I'm from Cleveland, but my name isn't Taylor. I'm not a general, either," he laughed. "Our driver fought in the Korean war and the only English he knows is 'Good morning, General Taylor. Would you like a Coca Cola?' "

"Oh," I said. "Then what rank are you?"

"What makes you think I'm not a civilian?" he asked.

"I don't know," Trudy said. "You're gallant and polite and not overweight."

"Besides," I said, "there are plenty of troops stationed here."

"There are also plenty of Americans here who

aren't in the service," he answered, avoiding the inter-
rogation. We were now nearing the town of Ephesus,
traveling on streets that were paved with beautiful
marble. Many buildings looked as though they had
been there for centuries; others looked as modern as
anything in the States. There seemed to be plenty of
soldiers and sailors trudging around, but as we neared
the center of town it began to look like St. Marks Place
in the East Village—hippies galore with their long
hair and beads and dungarees and ponchos and Indian
headbands.

"What are *they* doing here?" we inquired. Doug told
us Ephesus was a mecca for hippies from all over
Europe and America. Hashish was plentiful and
reasonably priced. "And, after all," he said mysteriously, "Turkey is one of the great opium producers of
the world. But I keep forgetting you've never been
here before. You'll love it, although I think you'll find
it's a man's country more than a woman's."

The Grand Hotel D'Ephese is beautiful and modern
and new, like a spot of Southern California dropped in
amongst the ancient ruins. It has a huge swimming
pool shaped like a gigantic fish and a bar downstairs
with a glass wall where the men can sit and wait for
the girls to pass by under water in their bikinis. Doug
explained the Germans had built it and thrown in a
few Turkish touches. When we arrived, the doorman
and the bellboys snapped to attention as if Doug were
a charter resident. Marc had arranged everything with
great precision, and our rooms were reserved and waiting. Doug was leaning over the desk, talking to the
clerk and trying to decipher the little cards on which
our room numbers were written. The clerk was playing the game, too, keeping the information just out of
Doug's view.

While they were playing games, another good-looking American came up and greeted Doug like a long

lost brother. There was something urgent he had to discuss with him, something that couldn't wait. Doug made a big show of introducing us.

"Father Lucian, may I present two friends of mine from the States. Miss Betty Crocker and Miss Elizabeth Arden." Trudy looked at me and I looked at her and we said we were charmed, enchanted, and so forth. We shook hands, North American style, keeping our distance, with no two-timing French kisses under the ear.

"Father Lucian is a Canadian," Doug explained. "He's the chaplain at the House of Mary just outside town. It's one of the big tourist attractions around here. You'll have to go and visit." Father Lucian seconded the motion.

"We certainly intend to," I said. "Maybe I could interest some of your girls in my eyeliners."

"Yes," said Trudy, "and I have some wonderful triple chocolate meringue cake mixes we're featuring this month in McCall's."

Father Lucian thought that we were very bright to come up with such impromptu repartee.

"They're actually over here investigating the hashish scandal in the Peace Corps," Doug confided to Father Lucian. "But they're pretending to be airline stewardesses on a layover from Athens."

"Ah, yes," said the self-styled Canadian padre.

This was the first half-truth I'd heard since landing at Ismir, and I wondered how he managed it. If Doug had spotted us as stews that meant he had to be some kind of spy himself. I hoped he was on our side, at least. It would be awful to think that someone this charming and helpful could be in the pay of an unfriendly power. Also, I had enough trouble with Trudy and that priest at the Vatican. I didn't want her getting entangled with another man of the cloth, even a would-be Canadian fake.

"Should we be cagey on the hotel telephone?" Trudy asked. "Will our room be bugged?"

"Naw," said gallant Doug. "They might open your mail. We taught them how to do that. Someone might listen in on the switchboard. But don't worry about bugs and taps. They don't have the equipment What's more, they don't *want* it. The spy game is too much fun. They'll never give way to machines. Never."

"Well, bully for them," said spy-struck Trudy. "I know just how they feel."

"We won't be getting any mail anyway," I said. "Nobody knows we're here."

"Nobody but the chief of police and the intelligence services of every major European and Asiatic power," said Doug.

"Well, anyway, we adore being followed," said Trudy. "But we don't like being bugged." I knew the boys had urgent hanky-panky to discuss and we had to freshen up. Before we could break away, however, Doug started making plans for dinner. Trudy was being over-eager so I gave her the all-clear.

"Why don't you two go ahead without me," I suggested. "I'm expecting to hear from Marc about tomorrow's schedule. I better stick close to the hotel."

"Sure you don't mind if I go the single girl route for tonight, Rachel?" Trudy asked. Shades of Rome!

"Go ahead, girl," I said. "Operate! We only have 48 hours."

While Trudy took a shower and wondered what she could wear for dinner to stun Doug into speechlessness, I took a look at the map in my purse to try and get oriented for tomorrow's photographic jaunt. I discovered that we had flown over the island of Lesbos to get to Ismir, which is really Smyrna, where the figs come from. And Ankara, the capital city, can be spelled Angora and that's probably where the

yarn comes from. And there's a river called the
Meander that wanders up or down from Istanbul,
which used to be Constantinople, and that's where
the English probably borrowed the verb meander
from. And Ismir is only a spit away from Gallipoli
where Winston Churchill had his own Bay of Pigs
disaster in 1916 or thereabouts.

And Philadelphia, like Ephesus, one-time capital
of the Eastern Roman Empire, is the site of one of the
seven churches of the Apocalypse all located on the
ancient royal road which we surely would be traveling tomorrow. And we thought *London* gave us a
sense of the past!

I was routed out of my historical reverie by a phone
call from Marc. He didn't seem to be at all impressed at what a miracle it was we had found our
way to the right hotel in the right town. He wanted
us to be ready to leave the hotel at eight o'clock in
the morning. He'd scouted the locations and got all
the government clearances from the police. But he
was very severe about certain instructions. He wanted
me in bed early. He was sending up two pills for
me to take; one to make me sleep and one to make
me make water. He wanted me to sleep with my
head high on a hard pillow and asked me not to drink
anything between now and when he finished shooting.

"Also, bring along a pair of heavy shoes. The heav-
iest walking shoes you have," he said. That was easy,
but the no drinking prohibition was tougher than anything I had endured as a stew. I thought he meant
no whisky. I asked him if I could have a glass of wine.

"Not wine. Not even *water*. And especially, no
Coca Cola. Not even coffee or tea."

"I'll do it," I finally agreed. "If you'll tell me why."

"It's a quick way of getting rid of puff in the face
and under the eyes."

I hadn't felt I was particularly bloated, especially

since I'd just lost seven pounds. "Never mind," he said. "Once you've seen the pictures you'll understand and thank me."

When I broke the news to Miss Baker that I was being quarantined for the night, she displayed all the disappointment of a teenager being told the chaperone for their school dance had been chloroformed.

I was in the tub when the bellboy arived to deliver my two pills. Gallant Doug had warned us the Turks have a double standard when it comes to foreign females. They frown on such things as minis and tight pants on the street, but the front pages of their local conservative newspapers are decked out with topless cheesecake. I tried to pull myself together, dripping wet as I was, before I opened the door. But even this young boy managed to undress me with his burning black eyes in a way that made Italians seem benign. I decided to skip dinner and piled into bed. The second pill hit me, and that's all I remember. I went out like a light.

It seemed only two seconds later that Trudy was back in the room, shaking me, slapping me and trying to force me to wake up and listen to some hysterical tale of woe. I was so foggy I barely noticed Gallant Doug was with her. They both tried to explain something to me in loud, shouted whispers. Then I noticed there was a third person with them, a young Turkish lad who didn't look over fifteen. At first, I thought it was the bellboy who'd leered at me when he got me out of the bath. Aha, I thought, he's a spy for the police. He's heard I'm a model and they want me to pose for the cheesecake cover of the local Police Gazette. Or maybe he's a scout for the local white slavers and they've come to make me an offer.

"You go ahead and have fun," I kept mumbling. "Don't worry about me. I just took a knock-out pill."

"Rachel, listen to me carefully," Trudy was whispering. "This boy is in trouble with the police. He's a friend of Father Lucian's. Father Lucian and Doug want to hide him in our room overnight until they can figure out some way to get him out to this British yacht in the harbor at Kusadasi. In the morning."

"What makes you think he'll be safe with me?" I said, looking him over. He had a face that was positively ravishing. Like a young Anthony Quinn. "Or what makes you think I'll be safe with him?"

"Don't be silly, Rach," Trudy was protesting. "Siri is madly in love with this young girl. Her family has arranged for her to marry someone else. She's threatened to commit suicide if she has to go through with it. And if Siri can stay out of police hands for six more days, maybe we can stop her from killing herself."

"I don't understand," I said. "In Turkey, girls want to shoot themselves *because* they're engaged. In the U.S., they want to shoot themselves because they're *not*."

"I don't understand it either, Rachel, but Doug and Father Lucian want to help him and I thought it was the least we could do."

"Uh huh," I said.

"We're leaving him here with you. We'll put the DO NOT DISTURB sign on the door. Doug says nobody will bother you."

"They better not," I said.

"We'll be back early. We're going out on the yacht for dinner to make ararngements about tomorrow."

"Goodnight, General Taylor," I heard myself saying, completely dopey. "Have a Coca Cola."

The next thing I remember was being awakened by an unholy racket outside the door of our room. I thought I was hallucinating. It seemed to me that an Army of men were jabbering, and half of them were rapping on the door. I reached for the light and couldn't find it. Sure. Sure. Doug said nobody would bother me and they'd put a DO NOT DISTURB sign on the doorknob. Some people just can't read.

"Trudy," I called out in a hoarse whisper. No answer. I tried to find the phone to call for help but I couldn't remember where it was. The place was dark as pitch. Suddenly, there was a flash of light and I could see Trudy at the door in her see-through nightie, about to unlatch the chain.

"Don't let anybody in, Trudy," I hollered. "I'll call the police."

"Don't bother," she said. "They're already here."

She undid the chain. I pulled the covers up to my chin, ready for the worst. The room was a mess. The luggage rack had been knocked over and my underthings were sprawled out in great array across a stretch of carpet. Trudy's robe was thrown across the dresser. A couple of hotel towels hung over a chair. If they intended to search our belongings for hashish or opium or military secrets, there was no rummaging to be done. Our lives were open suitcases. Our dirty laundry was all on display.

It wasn't until eight grinning, leering policemen crowded into our tiny room that I realized what they might be after. Something in my drugged-up brain told me they weren't looking for dope or microfilm or pictures. They were looking for the young Turk, young Anthony Quinn, the runaway Father Lucian asked us to hide. Now we were really in for it. Some-one had set us up real good and framed us and turned us in to the police. We'd be arrested, probably for something stupid and horrible like contributing to the delinquency of an Asian Minor.

The ranking policeman was gallantly helping Trudy on with her robe. He begged a thousand pardons

and excused himself for having to do his duty and
search the premises. It seemed to me Trudy was acting terribly dumb.

"Show them our passports. Explain we're American
citizens and tell them this is an outrage, Trudy,"
I suggested as I sat frozen in an upright position, the
scrapy chenille bedspread under my chin. Well, anyway, if they photograph us as we're being loaded
into the Turkish paddy wagon, I wouldn't be puffy.
And Marc would come looking for us in the morning.
When he found no trace, maybe he'd know what to
do. He got us into this mess. Now he could at least
do something towards bailing us out.

"Tell your friend no cause for alarm," the policeman was saying. "No cause for alarm. Nothing to
worry about. No bother. We have orders to search.
We must search."

One policeman took a position at each window.
With guns drawn, they peered into the courtyard
below. They flashed huge electric torches on the little
balconies outside the windows. The officer in charge
marched straight for the bathroom. The door was
locked. He tried it again. It was locked from the inside. I was holding my breath, knowing the jig was
up when I heard the lock snap. All eyes turned to the
door. The policeman held their guns at the ready
position.

"Good morning, General Taylor," I heard myself
saying. "Would you like a Coca Cola?" I must say
he had a beautiful tan. It was Gallant Doug in the
flesh, and nothing but the flesh.

He smiled and stepped out of the bathroom, retrieved a rumpled towel from the floor and draped
it around his untanned middle. I knew then that I
mustn't look surprised. After all, ours was a single
room with only two beds, and whatever had been go-

ing on, I must have been in on it. So I let go of the
bedspread I'd been clutching and thought about plead-
ing guilty to the lesser offense.

The police officers seemed totally delighted with
what they had interrupted. They removed their guns
from the ready position and began chattering among
themselves. Gallant Doug went into a huddle with
the commanding officer and made a show of putting
himself at his mercy and discretion. The policemen
gradually retired into the hall. The officer was the last
to leave. He tipped his hat and asked for a thousand
pardons. When Gallant Doug closed the door behind
them and put the chain back into position, it occurred to me that I wasn't drugged anymore. Neither
was I dreaming. I was wide awake and consumed with
curiosity about what was going to happen next.

Doug stayed with his ear to the door for a good
two minutes before turning around and giving us the
sign to be quiet. He tiptoed over to the windows and
closed the shutters. He gave me a big kiss and a
squeeze, then he got down on the carpet on all fours
and signalled to the frightened young Turk under my
bed that he could come out now.

"How long has he . . ." I started to ask before
remembering the need for silence.

"I don't think they'll bother us any more," Doug
whispered.

"I seem to remember you saying that earlier in the
evening," I said. "Or was it last night? How long has
this orgy been going on?"

Young Siri didn't say a word. He walked over to
one corner of the room, cased it like a puppy and
curled up and went to sleep on the floor. Trudy put
one of her pillows under his head and covered him
with a blanket.

I wondered what time it was but nobody seemed

to know. "Beddie bye time," Doug announced as he climbed into Trudy's bed.

"How are we gonna get them out of here?" I whispered to Trudy, thinking of the sleeping fugitive on the floor and the man in her bed. She didn't seem to think it presented any problem.

"The same way we got in," said Doug, making himself comfortable.

"Did you come through the halls in that towel?" I asked.

"No," said Doug. "My clothes are in the bathroom."

Doug explained he had bribed the assistant manager to let them bring young Siri to hide out in our room.

"He didn't stay bribed very long," I said. "He only let you bring him in so he could call the police and trap you."

"That's right," Doug said. "I knew he'd do that. He knew I knew he'd do it. That's why I didn't take any chances leaving him here alone with you. That's why I stayed here all night, too."

"You were here all *night?*" I said, raising my eyebrows as far as they would go.

"Yes, but I expected them earlier. It must have taken them quite a while to get organized."

"Are you sure you didn't bribe the police not to come too soon?" I asked.

"I didn't think of that," said Doug.

"So you'll have to bribe the manager again to sneak the boy out?"

"That's right," said Doug.

"And he'll call the police again and tell them where you're taking him," I suggested.

"He can tell the police, but they won't know where we're taking him. If *we* don't know where we're taking him, how can anybody else?" Doug concluded brilliantly.

"How about this yacht?" I asked. It seemed to me I remembered something about a yacht in the harbor . . . or maybe it was a helicopter on the lawn. My drugged stupor was getting all mixed up with my memories of all those James Bond movies.

Then Trudy went into rhapsodies about the dinner they had on this yacht in the harbor. It was owned by a British lady who had a Roumanian husband and they had a crew of eight in white uniforms plus a Lebanese Jesuit priest all in black, who travels everywhere with her. A private chaplain. I thought there was a shortage of priests and wondered how she could manage to have a private confessor of her own.

"Jackie Onassis has a yacht, but I never read about her having a priest in her crew," I said.

"She doesn't travel this far East," Doug suggested. "After all, when you have a port in Asia Minor and you have to go to confession, it could be very difficult. In Muslim countries, Catholic priests are very rare."

I really wasn't interested in the state of Christianity in Asia Minor. But I was curious about all the double-dealing and spying going on.

"Don't you get a little weary of living in a place where people lie all the time and play games, turning in one another to the police?" I asked Doug.

"When I first got here," he said, "I was like the other Americans, all hot and bothered about corruption. Not any more. Now I think the PX is the best foreign aid program we have. At least the leakage from the PXs reaches the people. Corruption is a game over here and if they play the game with American chips, that's the best kind of propaganda."

"But that doesn't mean the Army shouldn't try to stop it," I suggested naively.

"Oh, no, heaven forbid," said Doug. "If we didn't at least put up a show of trying to stamp out corruption, it wouldn't be any fun any more. It would deprive the people of any sense of accomplishment."

"I can understand that," Trudy said.

"The Black Market here is completely open and above board. You see some guy with his little stand and he has one bottle of every kind of booze. One Johnny Walker, one Vat 69, one J&B, and so on. And if the police come by on a raid, he shows them this legitimate customs receipt showing the duty has been paid on that one bottle. So there's nothing they can do. Teams of high-powered American sleuths come in and they mark all the PX supplies with secret ink. Then they come to the black market with their infra red lamps and they prove to the police that everything in the black market is contraband, lifted from the PX. The one bottle display gimmick is a game. Each time they sell a bottle, the dealer goes back to his stash and brings out another. One bottle, one customs receipt. When the Americans confront the police authorities with the results of their big operation with the secret ink and the ultra violet lamps, the authorities are fascinated with the whole thing. Look, the Americans tell them, you know what's going on, fellows? When are you going to knock this off? 'But, Douglas,' the Chief says to me, 'how do you expect me to live?' "

It came out then when I was least expecting it. It was practically an admission that Doug was some kind of American intelligence agent. On our side, thank heavens. Or maybe that whole spiel was just another diversion designed to throw me off. I couldn't let it drop.

"How can you operate as a spy if everyone knows who you are?" I said

"Who said I was a spy?" Doug asked innocently.

"You did. How can you investigate American

hanky-panky if everyone knows you're an investigator?" I wanted to know.

"They don't know what *rank* I am," Doug said triumphantly.

"You never get to wear your chicken on your shoulder?" Trudy asked. "Not even for formal dances and balls?"

That gave me an idea. I excused myself. One of my pills was working, I explained. I had to go to the bathroom. While I was there, I could go through his clothes, examine his wallet, leaf through his credit cards and his credentials. But he was too quick for me. He bounded out of bed and scurried into the bathroom.

"I forgot I left my things in a pile on the floor," he said.

"Don't be too long, Colonel," I pleaded. Foiled again, I thought, as he waltzed around in our bathroom and came out with his wardrobe over his arm.

When I finished my duties in the john I found our half-dressed Colonel on the telephone screaming at someone, demanding room service. He wanted breakfast for three and he was ordering doubles on everything.

"Isn't that slightly suspicious?" I asked.

"The poor kid must be starving," Doug said. "Besides, they'll expect us to be hungry after the police explain they interrupted our orgy.

As soon as Doug finished ordering our early morning banquet, he began planning our escape. When I explained that Marc was picking me up at eight for our location trip to Philadelphia, he invited himself along for the jaunt. He would arrange for Marc to take Siri along in his caravan. He and Trudy would follow along behind us. Once we got out near the Royal Road, they would transfer Siri to the trunk of Doug's car and take him out to this English lady's yacht where he would be out of reach of the police.

Within minutes, our room turned into Grand Central Station. Before the waiters arrived, Siri had to be hustled into the bathtub to hide. He didn't understand the plot completely and thought we wanted him to take a shower. I wanted to take a shower, but I couldn't begin while he was hiding in there. Doug wanted to dash off to his room to shave, but Trudy didn't want him to leave the room for a minute in case something unexpected happened, like a call from downstairs or a return visit from the police. So she got dressed and went to his room to fetch his shaving things. I was furious because I hadn't thought of that. I was too busy preparing for my assignment to think about my counter-espionage lessons. So I suggested that Trudy shouldn't be allowed to visit Doug's room alone. Suppose the police were waiting there and dragged her off for questioning or something. When I proposed we go together, Doug vetoed it. He knew I was only looking for a pretext to go through his drawers. So Siri took his shower and I stayed out of sight in the bathroom so I could burst into song to lead the waiter to believe I was in there taking a shower. Meanwhile, Trudy got dressed and got Doug a razor and clean shirt. When the food arrived, the poor young Turk was so starved he ate like there was no tomorrow.

Finally, Marc arrived. It was time to go. I wasn't exactly enjoying the notion of the four of us waltzing through the halls and lobby, maybe into the waiting arms of the police. So I insisted that Doug go ahead and case things and give us the all-clear on the telephone. Then I realized that would mean Siri would have to leave with *us,* and if they picked him up, we were the ones who would be accused of aiding and abetting his escape from the police. I was too nervous about our escapade even to think about being nervous about my first assignment as a would-be model. Siri was the only one who was the slightest bit calm. It was maddening. We were all going through these fantastic machinations in order to keep his little sweetheart from killing herself, and he sat, cool as a Turkish cucumber, coal-black eyes blazing, smiling and obviously enjoying watching us pull up and adjust our stretch panty hose.

Finally, Trudy was delegated to go ahead, like a pig through the minefields. She knew what Marc looked like; Doug didn't. As soon as Marc arrived, she was supposed to stay with him and send his assistant to our room to bring me down. This was intended to confuse the assistant manager in case he tried to count the number of people who left together.

Our exit plan worked like a charm. Trudy and I drove off with Doug in his American car. Marc and his assistant took Siri along in their rented station wagon with all the equipment and impedimenta. Doug settled on a rendezvous point outside of town. We stopped there while Siri was unloaded into the back seat of Doug's car. Doug and Trudy would take him directly to the yacht in the harbor at Kusadasi where he would safely sit out five more days of hiding. I drove off with Marc for the ruins near Philadelphia. We arranged to meet at the yacht after our location shooting was completed.

It turned out Marc had been in the French underground during the war. All this cloak and dagger stuff was like old home week for him. All you had to do was tell him somebody was trying to stay out of reach of the police and he knew what side he was on. I tried to explain the intricacies of Turkish law as it applied to arranged marriages, dowries and being an Asian minor, but it turned out Marc knew more about it than I did. He ended up educating me.

Our destination turned out to be a gigantic archeological digging expedition near Philadelphia. The spot looked like a movie set. The ancient pillars toppled over in pieces, centuries-old coins that would send any collector in frenzies were lying around on the hillside like beer cans in America, the age-old scars of earthquakes and wars left untouched as people moved on and rebuilt their homes somewhere else.

Marc had what looked like a beige safari shirt and slacks for me to wear. When he didn't like the look of my heavy shoes, one of his female assistants loaned me a pair with high laces and rubber soles. I didn't have to worry about my hair because Marc had a scarf from Paris he wanted tied around my head. He knew exactly what he wanted before he began. He had a pencil sketch of the entire lay-out, and he put me into place as if I were a paper doll. The only fly in the ointment was the wind across the hills. Marc was very efficient but that was something that couldn't be turned on and off. When he wanted the wind in my hair, nothing happened. When he wasn't ready, great clouds of dust appeared from nowhere in sudden gusts.

In a couple of hours the entire job was wrapped up and we were on our way back to the yacht. The harbor at Kusadasi was a sight to behold and there was only one yacht there. You couldn't miss it. This was my first visit to a floating palace of this size and splendor and I was excited the way some people get in their first flight on a plane.

A member of the crew was waiting with a little boat to putt-putt us out to the barge. Marc, ever wary of leaving his cameras and precious equipment, asked his assistant to stay on guard. I begged him to bring his camera along to take some pictures of me and Trudy in our moment of jet-set glory, but what professional photographer wants to take pictures in his leisure time? Besides it was perfectly clear the little yacht party wasn't impressing him in the slightest. Never mind, I thought, certainly Doug will have a camera. Who ever heard of an espionage agent without one of those little jobs that can photograph everything, night or day?

Trudy was waving frantically from the deck of the white yacht as we came into view. Everything had gone smoothly in all departments. Siri was safely stowed away in the crew's quarters. Our hostess had retired for a nap after lunch and Trudy had been having a ball as lone lady and center of attraction for three men; Doug, Father Lucian and a French Jesuit. They were all sunning themselves on the rear deck of the yacht. It was the first time I had ever seen two priests and an espionage agent stripped to the waist. You couldn't tell who was who without a scorecard. All three of them wore identical little medals around their necks on a silver chain.

"Wouldn't it be super if we could cruise back to Athens in a tugboat like this?" I said to Trudy. "I wouldn't care if I never saw another plane. Especially that T H Y divebomber."

Trudy agreed it would be a smashing idea but she felt that our hostess, the British lady who gave up her title (but not her money) to marry a Roumanian, was not too fond of female competition. "I think we're probably the only girls who've been near this yacht in ages."

"I can understand that," I said. "If this were my boat, I'd do the same thing."

We were all lounging on the sundeck when our eagle-eyed spy friend Douglas noticed a small boat coming along our side of the bay. He borrowed a pair of binoculars, took one look and went dashing for the crew's quarters below.

"What is it? What's wrong?" Trudy asked Doug.

"It looks like a police launch." He wasn't wrong. The launch pulled up near us and anchored. Then we saw the tallest Turk in captivity coming toward us in a little rowboat.

"Are you ready, Mata Hari?" I asked Trudy.

The Jesuit slipped into a full length white terry cloth monk's robe to receive the visitor on behalf of the hostess who was, as he explained it, resting. They exchanged politeness in Turkish for what seemed an endless amount of time while the tall Turk took careful note of us all. Finally, the Jesuit introduced us all around in English.

"Captain Habib is setting up a wild boar hunt and has invited all of us to be his guests," he explained. That was too exotic to be true. Father Lucian explained that the Turks were making a stab at trying to stir up tourist business and that was the province of Captain Habib, to dream up things which might intrigue wealthy jet-setters like our hostess.

Apparently, you can't offer a Muslim official an alcoholic drink without risking insult to him, his family and his ancestors, so we left the priests to entertain him. We were back on the sundeck with Marc when we heard a splash. Trudy looked at me and I looked at her. Now we could hear shouts of "Man overboard" in about three languages. It was several minutes before we could find out what happened. Someone was swimming frantically and splashing, not on the port side, toward the harbor as you might expect, but straight out into the open water.

The little police rowboat started after him. In a few minutes two uniformed police lifted a wet and dripping figure into the bottom of their small craft.

Father Lucian watched the incident with the binoculars, but never said a word.

I knew it was Siri. We found out later he had

panicked when he saw the police launch. He had seen the boat long before anyone else and was certain they were after him. Doug was too late to stop him. It seemed that young love could never win. It had been such a madcap comedy, such fun for us, to play spies for one night. Now it was going to have a grim ending, like a Turkish version of Romeo and Juliet.

There was nothing anybody could do. It cast such a pall over the party, everyone wanted to go to bed and brood. I forgot all about asking Doug to take some pictures of us. Soon it was time to scramble around and make the late afternoon plane.

Doug drove all of us to the airport at Smyrna. By that time he and Trudy were acting like an old married couple, so lovely-dovey and familiar. When I cursed the fates for not having any snapshots of our unbelievable afternoon, Doug said cryptically, "Don't worry. I'll send you plenty of photographs."

He was as good as his word. When we got back to New York several days later there was an airmail parcel waiting for us with an APO return address. Trudy tore it open avidly. In it were about forty of the most horrible photographs I had ever seen of myself. They all looked like a blow-up of a police mug shot. We couldn't figure out where he had taken them until we examined the background detail. Invisible cameras? His sporty American auto must have been completely equipped with invisible cameras that shoot you from four sides at the same time and you don't even know what's happening. They were marvelous top secret souvenirs of our adventures in James Bond country. And I do mean secret. I wouldn't want anyone to see them but my mother.

Doug had promised to keep us informed on the saga of Siri and his girl.

Trudy heard from him regularly, and for weeks he had nothing to report except that Siri was still in jail with his head shaved. He had tried to kill himself and his girl had tried to kill herself. But neither of them had been successful.

About three months later, Trudy got wonderful news. Doug reported that Siri was out of jail. It was, as he explained, a typical Turkish solution to a Turkish problem. Siri's parents negotiated with the parents of his girl for weeks. Then his girl's parents negotiated with the parents of her intended husband. Finally, after weeks of bargaining and wheedling, the parents of the intended groom were bought off.

Siri had his day in court and he swore on a stack of Korans that he was eighteen going on nineteen. He knew he was lying and his parents knew he was lying and her parents knew he was lying, and all the lawyers and the judge knew he was lying. But the unanimous acceptance of the lie turned it into an official fact and so they were married and lived happily ever after.

CHAPTER XVII

"The Passenger Is Always Right"

He was a big man, big and beefy. He wore the traditional businessman's costume—a gray suit, muted tie and black shoes. We had him pegged the minute he stepped on board as arrogant and demanding, one to avoid whenever possible. We develop a built-in radar after months of flying and dealing with the traveling public. It seldom breaks down.

"Miss!" he demanded the moment we were airborne.

"Yes, sir," I responded.

"Why were we late departing?"

"It was only a few minutes, sir. You see . . . "

"A few minutes, indeed. We were due to depart at nine. We didn't depart until nine twenty one. I'd like to know why."

"There was a delay in loading the meal service, sir. We're sorry."

"You should be. And this is the last time I ever travel with this airline."

"Yes, sir." I tried to get away but he kept right on talking, his face set in a heavy frown.

"The least you could have done was to inform us of the delay and the reason for it. You might at least have a little consideration for your paying passengers."

"Yes, sir, but we were busy and . . ."

"I'm sick and tired of excuses. I'm sick and tired of being shunted and bumped around. I'm a businessman and getting places is important to my work and my security. The least your airline could do is treat me like a human being and respect my needs."

"Yes, sir." I tried to escape again. This time he grabbed my arm.

"I'd also like to know why this cabin isn't cleaner. And it's too hot in here. I've been twisting this damned little nozzle and I'm still warm. I certainly expect a little more comfort and attention when I pay all this money to get somewhere. If you're going to provide bad service, then charge less for it. You and all the other airlines always going after fare increases. It's a crime to keep paying more and more and get less and less. This ashtray wasn't emptied. Why?"

"Well, sir, the cabin cleaners do the best they can with short turn-around service. And as for the fare increases, all the new equipment and the air congestion have placed the airlines in a bad financial situation."

"Nonsense. Rubbish. You'll be writing off these noisy damn jets in no time. Don't plead poverty with me. I know too much about this business to have the wool pulled over my eyes by the likes of you."

"Yes, sir. You certainly do seem to know a great deal about our business. Are you with an airline?"

"Hell, no. I wouldn't be caught dead working for one of these inefficient, sloppy outfits that bilks the working man."

"What *do* you do, sir?"

"Railroads. The biggest. I'm an Operations Manager for the Long Island Railroad."

"Yes, sir."

CHAPTER XVIII

"Welcome to the Bureaucracy"

Being an airline stewardess isn't nearly as much fun as it used to be. I don't mean that three or four years ago were more fun than today. I'm talking about twenty years ago, when stews were nurses and propellers drove the planes. Those were the days, we're told by former stewardesses who are now members of former airline stewardess clubs. Those were the days when on-board meals consisted of a pail of mashed potatoes, a pail of chicken, a pail of bread and a pail of green peas. Can you imagine being on one of those flights when the only thing placed aboard *your* aircraft was the pail of green peas, while another flight got all the chicken. Imagine, too, taking a day to get from New York to Chicago. Those were the good, old days for stewardesses because after such long flights, you had time to relax in the destination city before working another trip back.

Today, all of aviation has emerged into the world of science and speed. Aircraft are swift and sophisticated. Airline pilots fly by books and instruments, long ago having given up on the reliability of one's seat of the pants. Airplanes are everywhere, circling, stacked up, coming close, waiting in line, all of it. It's enough to send you back to the trains, if there were enough trains to go back to.

Today's aviation scene has caused a great deal of interest in Washington, D.C. There, in the halls of Congress and the offices of the Federal Aviation Administration, men apply knowledge and experience in solving aviation's growing set of ailments. It has become so complex and so challenging that, during one month last year, hands were thrown up in despair and heads shook in confusion. What was needed? Clearly, only the calm, steely logic of the airline stewardess could be counted upon to bring reason into the fray. Only the rock-steady determination of a stew could see through the smoke of imbroglio and find the answers. That's why Trudy and I were called to Washington as witnesses for a special aviation hearing.

You see, it had gotten so bad in our skies that only monumental changes could insure some sanity in the air transportation system. Congestion had become critical. Delays averaged two hours per flight. Forty near-misses were reported by pilots each day. Traffic jams in and out of airports took days to clear. The railroads began boasting the fastest coast-to-coast travel available to the public. It was horrendous. Only Congress could inject reason into the mess, and all eyes turned to the elected officials.

Of course, there were different interests to be served. Private pilots, afraid of being banned from the skies, had rallied behind their leading association, *The Society for the Prevention of Cruelty to Private Pilots.* The airlines rallied behind their spokesmen, *The Airline Spokesmen Association.* And in the middle stood that bastion of independent thought, the Federal Aviation Administration, commonly called the FAA. It had been their responsibility to insure safe and efficient air travel for all. Now, in the midst of chaos, this super-agency would be called upon to offer more opinions.

All parties would answer to Congress. Of course, everyone eventually answers to Congress anyway. But the delays had become insufferable. One member of Congress reported being delayed sixteen hours in flying between Washington, D.C., and his home, Atlanta. Other Congressional members had suffered similar fates, which prompted them to action.

Trudy and I assumed we'd been called to testify because of our long experience as stews, both domestic and international. Most stewardesses last only eighteen months on the job, snapped up by panting young men and led to the altar. We would join four other sisters of the skies before the committee. Also to testify were airline and private pilots, air traffic controllers, airport managers, mayors of leading cities and, of course, the spokesmen for the lobbying groups.

We checked in to Washington the day before the hearings were to begin, and were given rooms in the Hays Adams. They told us to relax. Relax? How? We were petrified at the thought of appearing. How does one act at a Congressional hearing? We'd watched some hoods appear on TV but they didn't impress us very much. Could we take the Fifth Amendment? No, that wouldn't look good.

"Just smile and answer the questions truthfully," George Kelman told us the night we left New York.

"But what if they ask us *hard* questions?"

"Just answer what you know," he said. "They don't expect you to be experts. Stop worrying."

We tried to relax. Trudy did sitting-up exercises on the floor while I rubbed a corner of the hotel bedspread and tried to read the paperback of *The Case Against Congress* in an attempt to gain insight into the men we'd be facing.

"They're crooks," I blurted out after a particularly impressive chapter.

"Who?" Trudy had turned to push-ups.

"Some of these guys in Congress."

"Watch it, Rach. If the room is bugged, J. Edgar Hoover will have you on the pink list by morning."

I mulled that possibility over and read on. Trudy

gave up exercising and turned to TV. The tension was building. I rubbed the bedspread harder; Trudy practiced her opening statement while an old movie played.

"Gentlemen, members of Congress and fellow citizens. I come before you in the interest of all that is pure and good in our democracy. I come here today . . ."

"For God's sake, Trudy, knock it off. That's corny."

Trudy agreed and tried different opening statements, all of which sounded equally bad. She finally gave it up, turning full attention to the movie, *Citizen Kane*.

After an hour of bedspread rubbing and Orson Welles, we had begun to relax. That mood was broken, however, when someone knocked on our door.

"Who is it?" I asked.

"Mrs. Lydia Jones. It's urgent that I speak with you."

"What about?"

"About the aviation hearings. I'm the president of the Wyoming Committee for Aviation Safety, a housewife organization. Please, may I come in?"

I looked at Trudy and she shrugged. Why not?

Mrs. Jones was a pretty little woman of about forty. She had a determined look in her eyes and spoke swiftly and without embellishment.

"I want you to hear this tape, Miss Jones and Miss Baker. I think you'll find it interesting."

"What's it about?" I asked.

"You'll see." She took a small cassette recorder from her oversize purse, pushed a button and voices began to play. We sat on the bed and listened.

"Senator Fillbruster, as you know the private pilot community has always delivered the vote for you back in Mississippi," a man's voice said. We both looked at

Mrs. Jones and she nodded smugly, indicating we were correct in assuming Senator Fillbruster was *the* Senator Fillbruster of Mississippi.

"Yes sir, ah know that," the Senator said. "Y'all know ah've always been on your side in all these aviation issues. Ah always vote for y'all."

"And we appreciate that, Senator."

"So how come y'all haven't gone and built that monument to me yet at the airport?"

"We're working on that, Senator. It takes time."

"Don't see why. The otha eleven monuments to me didn't take any time at all. Hell, ah remember when the folks from the Catholic lobby built that statue 'a me raght after ah voted for that bill they wanted. Built it raght next to the statue 'a Saint Patrick. 'Course, now that he ain't a saint no more it sorta waters down the importance 'a bein' next to him. But that ain't the point. It didn't take them no longer than three months to get that statue 'a me built and put up. Ah been votin' your way for six years and ah still don't see no statue."

"I didn't want to break the news at this time, Senator," the other gentleman said. "Because I didn't want it to appear I was currying favor with you with these hearings coming up. But we've assigned a sculptor to your project. He's a local boy *and* a private pilot. He's making sketches for our approval now."

"Say, that's damn good news, Pullwire. Damn good news. Just make sure this here boy 'a yours takes some special care on ma raght side. It looks a little grizzly over there sometimes."

I asked Mrs. Jones to stop the machine. She did, and I asked who this Pullwire was. Mrs. Jones explained he was I. Willard Pullwire, president of *The Society for the Prevention of Cruelty to Private Pilots* (TSFTPOCTPP). She clicked the tape recorder back on. The Senator was speaking again.

"Now, what's the situation over at the FAA, Pitot?" he asked. We again asked for the tape to be stopped and asked about Pitot. Mrs. Jones said he was Jimmy "Rollover" Pitot, a private pilot and an employee of the Federal Aviation Administration, commonly called the FAA.

"Roger and A-1, Senator," Mr. Pitot answered the Senator. "The heading's right on the nose."

"What in hell does that mean?" the Senator growled.

"It means, Senator, that we're still leaning towards the private aviation side of things. But these hearings are going to be trouble. You can bet your strut on that."

There was a moment of silence on the tape. The Senator broke the silence.

"How bad you figure things can get with these here hearings, Pitot?"

"Half and half, Senator. Your side could use some more altitude but the airlines are heading for a stall, too. Could be dual all the way."

"Goddammit, Pitot," Senator Fillbruster snapped. "Ah can't understand all that pilot lingo y'all use all the time. Talk plain!"

"Sorry, Senator."

Mr. Pullwire re-entered the conversation at this time.

"From my vantage point, Senator," he said, "I'd say that the forces are split about even. The older members of your committee are pretty much with us. The younger members seem to be against us, at least as far as we can determine from snooping around The Hill. It's hard to say what the other members of your committee will decide. Of course, you'd be in the best position to determine that."

"Ah used to know, but you can't be sure any more with these damn freshman upstarts."

Pullwire seemed to lean closer to the microphone. I started to ask Mrs. Jones how she got this recording, but she silenced me with a finger to her lips.

"We've been analyzing the situation, Senator," Pullwire said, "and we feel it's going to take some little thing, some tiny edge to tip things in our favor and to make sure the skies are kept free for everyone. We've talked a great deal about this and have decided it might just be these stewardesses testifying who make the difference."

We could hear the Senator laugh heartily. "Stewardesses?" he said. "Hell, as far as ah'm concerned, they ain't gonna be worth Mississippi mud in the hearings. Why in hell all these damn committee members insisted on havin' them testify is a mystery to me."

Mr. Pullwire explained that since aviation had reached a breaking point, those members of the committee wanted everyone to have a chance to make their views known.

"Ah know, ah know, Pullwire," Senator Fillbruster coughed. "But what makes y'all think what they say is gonna make any damn difference at all?"

"Because they're young and pretty and well-meaning. They haven't got any bones to pick, and that makes them believable. Stewardesses generally don't have many opinions on anything Therefore, I've already sent some of my best people to talk with the stewardesses called to testify. We'll be working on them in our usual subtle manner, Senator. By tomorrow, they'll be on our side, I have no doubt of that."

"Sounds good, Pullwire," the Senator said. "Ah'll certainly be doin' mah part for y'all. Always have."

"Yes sir, Senator, you certainly have done your part to insure freedom of the skies. And I might add I'm very relieved you're chairing the committee tomorrow.

At least someone will be able to step in and put things on the right track."

The tape ended with the scuffling of chairs and vague good-byes. Trudy and I were shocked, stunned. We both looked to Mrs. Jones, but she said nothing. Finally, Trudy asked, "What do we do, Mrs. Jones?"

"Nothing, girls. That's why I arranged to have that meeting recorded by a friend who works as a waiter in the restaurant where it was held. I wanted you and the other girls to hear the kind of hanky-panky going on behind the scenes of aviation. Now that you've heard it, I know you'll act accordingly. Of course, you must never mention this tape. I only played it for you so you wouldn't be taken off guard by some of the forces at work here."

We promised we wouldn't, thanked her for coming and let her out of the room. We started to discuss the situation when the phone rang.

"Miss Jones?"

"Yes."

"This is Richard Wheedle, Miss Jones. I'm an official greeter for TSFTPOCTPP."

"What's that?" I knew, of course.

"A society of concerned aviation people. We're aviation folks, just like you."

"I see. What can I do for you?"

"Well, we know you and your fellow-stewardesses have come to Washington to help in solving aviation's problems, and we'd like to make sure your stay is comfortable. I've already contacted another stewardess, Miss Whoopsman, and she's having dinner with a few of us. I'd like to invite you and Miss Baker, too."

I accepted. After hearing the tape I felt secure that neither Trudy nor I could be influenced. And, I wanted to see first-hand, how these things were done.

I discussed the invitation with Trudy after the phone conversation was over, and we agreed it would be wise and interesting to go through with it. In fact, it was downright James Bond.

The limousine driver took us to a fashionable restaurant. Already present were Mr. Wheedle, an assistant, and two other stews. One was Miss Whoopsman. We chatted with her for a few minutes over a drink and came to the conclusion she represented the last of the great ambivalent creatures. She agreed with anything being said at the time, including all opinions expressed during a single conversation. I mentioned how beautiful I thought Washington was.

"Yes, it certainly is," Miss Whoopsman agreed.

"I don't know," Trudy said. "It doesn't seem that beautiful to me."

"I know what you mean, Trudy," Whoopsman said. "Not so beautiful."

I told them I was frightened of the hearings.

"What's the big deal?" the fourth stewardess asked. "It doesn't frighten me one bit."

Whoopsman had agreed with me it was frightening. She also agreed with the other stew that it wasn't any big deal and there was nothing to be frightened of.

We sat down to dinner. The appetizer was a shrimp cocktail. "I love shrimp," I said.

"Me, too," Whoopsman hastily concurred.

"I hate it," the fourth stew said.

"Shrimp really aren't very good," Whoopsman said.

And so it went. We did find out that Miss Whoopsman had been especially requested for the hearings by the committee chairman, Senator Fillbruster. It seems they'd met once on a flight and the Senator complimented Whoopsman on her ability to see both sides of everything. He made sure she would be a witness. The fourth stew, a hard cookie from a domestic airline by the name of Darlene De Sade, told us how the rest of us were picked.

"Computer," she mumbled, her mouth full of lettuce. "The committee gave the airlines profiles of the kind of stews they wanted as witnesses and it was run through the computer." It was all very degrading; we had assumed we'd been chosen for more esoteric reasons.

Mr. Wheedle was very relaxed and pleasant at dinner. He joked about everything but aviation. Finally, right after dessert was served, he stood up and began conducting the rest of the evening. He gave a little speech on the state of aviation today, saying it was at the crossroads. And then he showed us a movie. I felt like a captive at one of those free Florida real estate dinners, where the movie is always shown of people having fun in a swamp. This film was about private pilots. It featured a lot of great couples flying around and kissing and enjoying flying as a family activity.

The final scene showed a happy young man in a cardigan sweater with his smiling wife, two freckle-faced children and an Irish Setter dog. They romped away from the camera towards a shiny red airplane, the narrator asking, "Could this man be a menace?"

The lights came up and Mr. Wheedle led the applause. He explained away the film as entertainment, to get us in the mood for the hearings. By that time, I was only in the mood for my room, bed and sleep. Trudy felt the same. But that was not in the evening's plans. Wheedle announced we would all proceed to a favorite spot of his, a jazz club called Blues Alley. "It's a great place to relax and unwind," he told us. There's no need to go into the details of the hour at Blues Alley. Great place, sensational music and a boring table with Wheedle, De Sade and

Whoopsman. We got back to the hotel at midnight and received a last-minute bit of advice from Wheedle.

"Remember, girls, tomorrow could well mark the most crucial moment for all of us in aviation. Our whole concept of democracy is built upon freedom for the little guy, little guys like you and me and your brothers and sisters. Don't ever let the big guys deny that freedom to anyone."

His words conjured up visions of the young man and his family running towards that little airplane. How could our airline work towards his destruction? I felt ashamed about the whole situation. I expressed my feelings to Whoopsman on the way up in the elevator. She, of course, agreed with me. It was Trudy who hadn't been lured into this train of thought.

"Nonsense," she said.

"I was thinking that, too," Whoopsman said.

The night's sleep was a fitful one. I dreamed I was chained to a post while Congressmen fired questions at me. For each answer I gave that didn't jibe with what they wanted to hear, I was whipped. Trudy stood by laughing at me because she'd given all the right answers and had been unchained. Whoopsman was sitting on the committee, of all things, and she asked me the hardest questions. It was impossible to give her the right answer because she always thought of the other side, making me constantly wrong. And who was whipping me but Darlene De Sade, who'd won that coveted post by sleeping with Mr. Wheedle. It was horrible.

"I take the Fifth," I woke up screaming.

"Bourbon or Scotch?" Trudy asked from her bed. I looked at my watch. It was eight o'clock; the sun streamed in the windows and the hearings would begin at ten.

We arrived at the building where the hearings were

to be held and discovered we were only two of hundreds of witnesses. They told us we'd be called in the afternoon, but it was suggested that we attend the morning session and get an idea of the procedures. We sat in a gallery reserved for witnesses and watched as Senator Fillbruster called the hearings to order and questioned the first witness, a pilot for an airline. He seemed very nervous but managed to answer the questions with some sense of authority. Senator Fillbruster took exception to some of his answers, especially when they indicated the pilot had experienced many near misses with private planes.

"Now just a moment, captain," the Senator said, "Just what in tarnation do y'all consider a near miss?"

"When I have to take a violent evasive action to avoid the plane," the captain answered, bringing a few snickers from the audience.

"Well, now, just what do y'all mean by violent?"

"Violent, Senator. Sudden."

"But not so violent that y'all can't be sittin' here today. Not so violent that y'all went into the ground."

"No sir, but . . ."

"Ah'm finished with this witness. Thank you for comin' here this mornin'." The captain tried to say something else but was ushered from the stand while the next witness, a manager of a private airport, was called. He told the committee that the pilots using his airfield were well-trained and competent. A young Congressman asked about the statistics on how many private pilots drank whiskey before they flew.

"A couple, I guess. No law against it."

"No law against it?" The young Congressman was appalled.

"No, sir. Just a rule against flying the plane while under the influence of alcohol. Most of the fellas I know hold their liquor pretty well. I've never seen them under the influence."

The hearings continued.

At lunch, in a cafeteria across the street, we sat with Whoopsman and De Sade. Soon, we were approached by Mr. Wheedle.

"Everything nice and tasty, girls?"

"Oh, yes," Trudy answered, gagging on a piece of petrified fruit from her fruit Jello.

"Good, good. Nothing too good for our stewardesses. Are you all ready for this afternoon?"

"Well, we're here. I guess that means we're ready," De Sade said.

"Good. Wonderful. And just don't forget the little guy. He's just like you and me."

Wheedle walked away and De Sade muttered, "I don't like that creep." Trudy and I agreed, but to our surprise, Whoopsman said she thought he was nice. Her stand was encouraging. Maybe there was hope for her after all.

Trudy was called first when the committee reconvened for the afternoon session. Senator Fillbruster was very nice to her, as were the other committee members. They asked about her experiences with delays and passenger reactions.

"Most passengers are so tired just trying to get somewhere," she answered, "they never bother to complain."

"Then y'all might say they aren't bein' inconvenienced as much as we might be led to think they are?" Fillbruster concluded.

"I don't mean that, sir. What I mean is . . ."

"Yes. Well, now, let's get ourselves on to anotha question . . ."

That's the way it went for the rest of the afternoon. They questioned Trudy for an hour, but Senator Fillbruster never really allowed her to express herself. Other committee members tried to press further whenever Trudy would begin to say something interesting, but Fillbruster's big, foghorn voice and imposing manner shut off all meaningful questioning. At times, I. Willard Pullwire could be seen nodding and smiling at the Senator from his seat in the witness gallery. Wheedle nodded in syncopation.

After Trudy, they called Mr. Pitot. He took the stand, wearing green aviator glasses and flap-pocket pants. He was asked if, as a member of the FAA's staff, he felt private planes were a contributing factor to the day's aviation ills.

"No, sir, I don't think so. From our experience at the FAA, the private planes don't pose any problem at all." Pitot looked up to Pullwire and received the nod and smile of approval. He pulled out a flight computer and played with it as he continued his testimony. "In fact, Senator, it's my judgment—and I might say the judgment of many of my colleagues— that if private aviation folks were allowed to run the airways, things would be in a lot better shape than they are now. Let me tell you why. You go out to any airport and there are those big jets belchin' smoke and makin' all that noise and flyin' around too fast and you can't help wonderin' if they ought to be there at all." Pitot's eyes had glazed. He was breathing deeply and whirling the flight computer faster and faster. Pullwire's smile had turned into a concerned frown, and he slowly shook his head back and forth, hoping Pitot would look up. Senator Fillbruster had taken a coughing fit, but Pitot didn't seem to notice.

"You ought to try it some day, Senator. All of you ought to try it. You all ought to come out to the airport and look around. You come out there like I do and breathe in those good fumes from the Pipers and Cessnas and take off your jackets and run your hand over the metal and pull out a dip stick. Check the oil. Run up the magnetos and hear it purr, really purrrrr, and then you know who belongs there and in the

skies." Pitot dropped the computer and began making
flying maneuvers in the air over the microphone. "Lots
'a times I get on my cycle and slip into that soft leather
jacket and get out there to the field. Oh, it's somethin'
else. Really full throttle."

Fillbruster coughed longer and louder and finally
managed to shut Pitot up. "We're certainly pleased
that y'all could come here, today, Mr. Pitot. Thank
you."

"My pleasure, Senator. I'd do anything and go anywhere to keep the little guys free up there." He
pointed to the ceiling. "Free to challenge the gods and
bore holes in the blue. Free to pull back on that stick
and get the wheels up and head for that nearest silver
cloud. Free to . . ."

Violent coughing.

". . . go where man never went before. A plane's
like a good woman, if you'll pardon me, Senator.
Right there when you push the button and pour it on
full-bore, right to the fire-wall."

"You're excused, Mr. Pitot."

"Yes, sir. And never forget we at the FAA will
never let those big jets take away the wild blue
yonder from ANYBODY!!" He was hysterical, shaking
and waving his arms and making airplane noises.

"Ah think this might be a good time for us all to
adjourn this here hearin' for the day. We'll start up
again tomorrow mornin' at ten." Pullwire had already
left the gallery and raced across the street to the Senator's offices. Pitot was interviewed outside in the
corridor by the press. His hysteria had abated and he
was calmly assuring everyone the FAA was dedicated
to safety in the skies for all mankind.

We went back to the hotel with Whoopsman. Darlene De Sade informed us she had a date and wouldn't
be back until late that night. As we were riding up in
the hotel elevator, Whoopsman began to cry.

"What's the matter?"

"I'm so scared, I'm shaking inside."

We took her to our room and poured her a stiff drink. It seemed to relax her a little and she became talkative. She told us of her childhood and two years of college and how she was never capable of having an opinion on anything. We tried to comfort her, but she just started crying all over again and said she was tired and needed a nap. She went to her room, leaving us to shower, nap, have dinner in the room and be in bed by nine.

The hearings resumed promptly at ten the next morning. Darlene was the first witness called and she gave short, snappy answers to every question. Unfortunately, she gave cynical answers to questions about private pilots.

"What's been your experience with private pilots, Miss De Sade?" a committee member asked.

"Oh, I think they're just about the nicest, most manly gentlemen I've ever met." The committee didn't catch the sarcasm in her voice and accepted her testimony as favorable to the private side of things.

The morning passed without me being called. I finally reached the witness stand late in the day. They didn't ask me very much. It seemed the other members of the committee had lost interest. Only Senator Fillbruster pressed on, leading me into answers I really didn't want to give. They excused me after fifteen minutes.

Trudy and I went back to New York and resumed flying. We kept track of the hearings as they were reported on radio and television. We often questioned why we hadn't heard of Whoopsman's testimony, but those thoughts were laid to rest when, on a Friday evening, the TV networks carried live coverage of the final session of the hearings. We watched with great interest, especially at the testimony of I. Willard Pullwire, and finally, Stewardess Whoopsman. Pullwire had given an impassioned speech about freedom of the skies. The cameras often caught Senator Fillbruster's reaction to the speech. He couldn't have been more pleased.

We were very upset when Whoopsman took the stand. The TV commentator commented after Pullwire's testimony that throughout the hearings, the positions taken by the private aviation sector of the aviation community had been more favorably received. It was the commentator's opinion that if the committee reacted to the testimony as presented, it would be hardpressed to do anything but propose new rules broadening private aviation's operations, and restricting the operations of the airlines.

"Now, Miss Whoopsman," Senator Fillbruster began, "we want y'all to relax and just answer our questions." Whoopsman seemed so flustered, so ill-at-ease, so vulnerable. We ached for her, knowing that the Senator would simply have her say the things he wanted her to say. He gave her a fatherly smile and said, "Ah think we've all sort 'a come to realize that the problems in aviation today have to do with too many big jets pollutin' the air and makin' noise and fillin' the skies up. Ah imagine that's about how y'all been seein' it too."

"Yes sir, I guess that's right."

"Haven't you been delayed many times by private planes, Miss Whoopsman?" a young Congressman asked.

"Yes sir, I guess that's right, also."

"Now, now, Miss Whoopsman, there's no need for y'all to become flustered. Y'all just relax and answer *mah* questions."

Senator Fillbruster continued to lead Whoopsman along. Other committee members would break in and try to set the record straight, but they were stymied

by the Senator and Miss Whoopsman's willingness to
go with the strength, in this case, Senator Fillbruster.

It was all very boring, and we were about to turn
off the coverage when a strange thing happened.
Whoopsman sat up straight in her chair, took a deep
breath and answered what was to be the Senator's
final question. It was, "Y'all are obviously a good
American. And certainly, as a good American, y'all
want to see every individual receive his freedom. After
all, that's what this fair democracy is all about, isn't
it?"

"Yes sir, it is. But . . ."

"But what, Miss Whoopsman?" another committee
member asked.

"But . . . but I don't think it applies here. I
think . . ."

"Thank you Miss Whoopsman for appearin' here
for the committee," Senator Fillbruster said.

"Wait a minute," the other committee member said,
waving his hand. "I'd like to hear what Miss Whoopsman was about to say."

"I was just going to say that . . . that . . . that I
think it's terrible the way all those private planes and
private pilots fly around and endanger every passenger
who takes a flight on an airline. Studies show that 30
per cent of fatal private plane accidents have pilots
with high blood alcohol levels. They don't receive
enough training. The planes aren't equipped right.
They fly into busy areas without even telling anybody.
I just think it's awful the way millions of passengers
pay for the airways system and never have anything
to say about it. I think it's time their rights were considered, and . . . and . . . I'm sorry." Whoopsman
cried. Fillbruster looked like he was going to cry, too.
And everyone applauded her statement, including us
in our apartment.

A few months later, the committee issued its recommendations. It was a unanimous proposal, except for Senator Fillbruster, who issued his own minority report. Basically, his majority report called for increased regulation over every phase of private aviation. Every phase. Everyone in the airline business applauded the recommendation. They remained buoyed up until the FAA acted upon the committee's recommendations. The agency restricted airline flights to 70 per cent of what they had been, and cited the Federal Aviation Act of 1958 in which every citizen was assured freedom of the skies. And, to top it off, they passed a new regulation under which you can become a private pilot in only thirty hours, as opposed to the previous thirty-five-hour requirement. Congress, by this time, had turned to the problem of water pollution, and was holding hearings on the subject.

CHAPTER XIX

"No More Diaries"

A few months later, it was Christmas. It had been a long year, lots of fun, but long. Our diary was filled with notes of the foreign places we'd visited and the people we'd met and enjoyed. Our agent for the original *Coffee Tea or Me?*, Sean O'Malley, had read the diary and had interested various publishers in our newest memoirs. Everything was looking up, including the gala New Year's Eve party to be thrown by our favorite stew bum, George Kelman. He'd rented an entire bar on the East Side and had invited 100 people, most of them known to us. We shopped for the most expensive party dresses of our lives (our agent assured us there would be a decent advance on the new book), and we couldn't wait for December 31 and George's bash.

We weren't disappointed. The party was a smash. Everyone enjoyed himself, dancing and singing and kissing and hugging and having a ball. After the midnight ceremonies were over and everyone settled down to some serious drinking and dancing, George climbed up on the bar and called for quiet. It took a while for everyone to pay attention, but eventually a hush fell over the room.

"Everybody listen," George said, weaving slightly under the Tiffany lamps. "I have a very important announcement to make."

"Hooray," a drunk yelled.

"Shut up."

George cleared his throat and continued. "As most of you know, Rachel and Trudy are not only two of the best damned stews in the sky, they're also the authors of a famous book."

Everybody whistled and applauded except one guy who muttered something about the book not having redeeming social value.

"But most of you don't know that our two little flying writers are ready to do another book based on their year flying overseas. They kept a diary and some diary it turned out to be."

More applause.

"So, in light of this, and because I love them so dearly, I've got a little present for them." He held up a small package wrapped in festive red and green. I went up on the bar and stood next to him.

"Here you are, Rach," he said handing the package to me. I smiled nervously and opened it. Then my smile disappeared.

"What is it?" everyone yelled.

"A diary," I answered.

"A diary?" Trudy shrieked.

"Yup," I yelled back. "A 1970 diary. Leather, too."

George beamed.

"To keep the notes for the next book, Rach."

I hugged George Kelman and gave him a great big kiss. Trudy jumped up on the bar and kissed him, too. We led him to a table and sat him down between us.

"George."

"Yeah?"

"We love the gift and the thought behind it."

"Oh, yeah. It seemed perfect."

"Well, it would be, except for one thing."

"What's that, Rach?"

"We're not keeping a diary any more. There isn't going to be a third book. In fact, we're quitting as stews."

He was stunned. This old-time stew bum was incapable of speaking.

"You see, George, we've decided that four years of administering to babies and drunks and aggressive captains is plenty. It's been a ball, but enough's enough. Trudy's getting married. And me? Well, I think I'll try the field in some other business. Maybe I just wasn't destined to find a guy in the sky. I'm ready to get down to earth."

George's eyes filled up and he had to struggle to keep back the tears, encouraged by too much whiskey and dancing and partying.

"No more?" he asked.

"No more," I answered.

He pulled himself up tall in the chair and managed a smile. "Well, I guess they call that progress," he said. "On to better things for you two."

"It's nice of you to think of it that way, George. And here, take this." I handed him the leather diary.

"No, that's my gift to you."

"We know that, George, but we'd rather have you keep it. If we have it, we might be tempted to use it. In your hands, it'll find good use." He accepted the diary back from us, rose, and started to walk back to the center of the partying. He stopped after a few steps, turned, and yelled back, "I'll miss you two."